S0-AHE-250

STANDARDS
and
SPECIFICATIONS

INFORMATION SOURCES

MANAGEMENT INFORMATION GUIDE : : 6

STANDARDS and SPECIFICATIONS

INFORMATION SOURCES

Erasmus J. Struglia

[Librarian
Consumers Union of U.S., Inc.]

Preface By
Roger E. Gay
Managing Director
American Standards Association

A Guide to Literature and to Public and Private Agencies Concerned with Technological Uniformities

GALE RESEARCH COMPANY • BOOK TOWER • DETROIT, MICHIGAN

OTHER GALE PUBLICATIONS

Library of Congress Catalog Card Number 65-24659

$8.75

CONTENTS

FOREWORD

Management processes continue to grow more complex and the range of factors relevant to contemporary decision-making mounts apace. Inevitably, the volume of published information and the number of institutions and agencies which aid in the identification of factual material, increases correspondingly. The variety of materials, publications, and institutions useful in providing the factual basis for informed management judgments varies considerably from one field to another. Often, the businessman, government official, student, and librarian will lack a comprehensive and organized inventory of the resources available for fact finding in a particular field. One inevitable consequence is that the opportunity to apply appropriate factual information to the problem-solving process may be lost.

The "Management Information Guide Series" is being developed expressly in order to overcome this deficiency in basic business research tools. Each volume is edited by one or more individuals known to be expert in the subject matter of the field as well as in the information resources applicable to the problems of that field. Each is devoted to a topic of broad interest to business and professional personnel. Each work in the series is designed to direct the user to key sources by arranging, describing, and indexing published sources as well as the programs and services of organizations, agencies and facilities, which in combination make up the total information scene of each of the fields covered.

Paul Wasserman
Series Editor

PREFACE

Peering out through what Mr. Struglia might call a clearing in the heart of the "jungle enshrouded in a white mist," we who are engaged in standardization work see a rather different vista.

It is indeed true, as this extensive and admirably ambitious work so amply demonstrates, that there are many originators of standards and numerous organizations and groups engaged in standardization activities here in the United States as well as throughout the entire world. This is a great tribute to the dynamic nature of modern society.

But it may be a mistake to liken to jungle denizens the many thousands of individuals who seek solutions to their scientific, technological, industrial and commercial problems through the highly systematic procedures of rational standardization. The energetic and purposeful efforts of these individuals and the associations, technical societies, companies and institutions which they represent are made within the framework of our free society.

Standardization in the United States must, by the very dictates of our free enterprise system, be compatible with the democratic process and with the freedom of the individual to choose the activities he thinks worthy of his efforts. This is the precise reason why the American Standards Association (ASA), the national organization for voluntary standardization in the United States, was originally established. Serving as the national clearinghouse and coordinating agency for the voluntary development and application of standards, ASA is an organization belonging to all American interests, a federation of trade associations, and professional societies, having more than 2,000 company members as well.

What is of major importance, however, is that full coordination in standardization activities is attained in the development of American Standards. A standard is termed an American Standard when accepted by a consensus of all national groups substantially concerned with its scope and provisions.

If there seems to be a "jungle" of standardization activities, it is because the rate of coordination at the national level has not kept pace with the proliferation of standards at the company, industry and technical society levels to the extent that has become necessary to best serve the needs of the nation. Recent developments in industry-government review of national standardization hold out the promise of greater cooperation and coordination between major groups involved in standardization activities in this country.

Mr. Struglia must be complimented and congratulated on his diligent attempts to cope with so vast a literature as that of standardization. His work has been successful, and I am certain that this guide will prove to be extremely useful both as an introduction to the field and as a tool for the more seasoned practitioners for a long while to come.

March 1965

Roger E. Gay
Managing Director
American Standards Association

INTRODUCTION

Standards and specifications and the agencies that produce them have multiplied at a rapid rate in our twentieth century industrial-technological milieu. This growth attests to the incontrovertible need for standards in evolving technological societies. It does not mean that any existing technological society is operating under a rational system of standards, except in the areas of basic weights and measures and in systems of nomenclature. Nor does it mean that the role of standards in our society is properly understood. T. A. Marshall, Executive Secretary of the American Society for Testing and Materials, declared that one of three major problems in the field of standards was "a lack of proper understanding by management--and I mean high management--of the importance and significance of standardization...This lack of understanding affects every phase of standardization work."[1]

Economist Robert A. Brady, in his cogent study of the scientific revolution in industry expressed like sentiments: "...It would be difficult to cite a single instance in the whole history of the rise of modern industrial methods where the need for complete, exhaustive, and painstaking reexamination is more badly needed than here. Scientists have given standards the most support. Engineers have shown increasing interest. Economists are almost unaware of its problems. Aside from a narrow range of industries, industrialists have paid it relatively little attention. Trade and distribution have almost entirely by-

---

1. SOME IMPORTANT PROBLEMS OF STANDARDIZING SOCIETIES. MATERIALS RESEARCH & STANDARDS 4: 304, June 1964.

passed its issues or taken a hostile position toward it. Ultimate consumers scarcely know the meaning of the word."[2]

Hopefully, industrial managers will achieve this understanding by a studied approach to the problem, rather than have misunderstanding thrust upon them by a complexity of pressures from without. The pressures are most certainly mounting--the irreversible trend towards automatic control of processes; the concern over depletion of natural resources; the exigencies of more highly competitive international trade; stepped-up demands by consumers for product information that will more accurately equate quality with price; and, finally, the role of governments, national and state.

The proliferation of standards and standards-making bodies without the presence of a rational system of standards gives our standardization activities somewhat the aspect of a jungle enshrouded in a light mist. The compilation of this book was based upon a cheerful assumption by author, editor and publisher that it would serve as a useful guide through this jungle.

October 1964 E. J. Struglia

2. ORGANIZATION, AUTOMATION, AND SOCIETY. Berkeley and Los Angeles, University of California Press, 1961. p. 142.

Section 1

GENERAL SOURCES AND DIRECTORIES

Section 1

GENERAL SOURCES AND DIRECTORIES

A comprehensive handbook of essential data does not exist for standards and specifications. The gap is slowly being filled by means of a cooperative project recently undertaken by the Standards Engineers Society, members of which have volunteered to prepare sections dealing with history and theory, basic principles and applications of standards, company standardization, standards subject to legal adoption, national and international standards, as well as literature and directory information. Sections are being issued as they are completed, the one designated as Section 5.4, Physical Standards, having been published as an insert in the June/July 1964 number of STANDARDS ENGINEERING, monthly publication of the Standards Engineers Society. One of the main features of Section 5.4 is a comprehensive listing of units of measure and their conversion to other units. There are 100 reference books listed in the bibliography. General measurement as well as electrical, electronic, microwave, and mechanical measurement books are included.

A major aspect of standardization--standards in industry--is excellently covered in:

Melnitsky, Benjamin. PROFITING FROM INDUSTRIAL STANDARDIZATION. New York: Conover-Mast, 1953. 381 p.
The underlying theme is that standards have value because they produce profits. The 25 chapters include a history of industrial standards; sources of industry, national and government standards; organization of the company standards department; developing, preparing and making the most of company standards; standards of measurement; preferred numbers and modular coordination; standards of

> identification; classification; part numbering; physical identification; standard parts; standard engineering materials; design standards; specifications and testing; purchase standards; and standardizing the human element.

A 433-page document on standardization activities in the United States was prepared in 1941 by S. P. Kaidanovsky for the congressionally-appointed Temporary National Economic Committee. Designated as Monograph N. 24, CONSUMER STANDARDS, it describes the standardization, inspection and labeling activities of Federal agencies, companies, trade associations and technical societies; standardization and simplification of products as affected by state legislation; value of standards, grades and informative labels to consumers and their effect on merchandising; recommendations and policies of various organizations relating to consumer standards, grading and labeling.

In 1960 a special advisory committee of the National Academy of Sciences submitted to the Secretary of Commerce a report entitled THE ROLE OF THE DEPARTMENT OF COMMERCE IN SCIENCE AND TECHNOLOGY (157 p.), but generally referred to as the Kelly report after the name of the committee chairman. Among the various recommendations of the committee was the following:

> "That the Secretary of Commerce take the leadership in initiating another study of standardization in the United States by an appropriately constituted body for the purpose of strengthening and unifying the standards and simplified practices program of the nation."

Acting on the recommendations of the Kelly committee, J. Herbert Holloman, Assistant Secretary of Commerce for Science and Technology, early in 1964 set up an advisory Panel on Engineering and Commodity Standards whose purpose "is to review the broad requirements for industrial and commodity standards in the United States and to make recommendations as to activities important to meeting national requirements for standards, with particular emphasis on the role of the Federal Government and the Department of Commerce. It will be important to give special attention to the relationship between activities of the private standards groups and the Federal Government and to the problem of international standards." The Panel, headed by Francis L. LaQue, vice-president of The International Nickel Company, has

prepared a report which was presented to Secretary of Commerce, John T. Connor, on March 4, 1965. It is available from the Clearinghouse for Federal Scientific and Technical Information, Springfield, Va. Section A presents findings and recommendations. Section B contains Task Force Reports on the roles of trade associations, technical societies, government agencies, and the American Standards Association in standardization. A major recommendation of the Panel is for the enactment of legislation establishing an Institute to serve as a national coordinating body for standardization, preferably by reconstituting the A.S.A. under Federal Charter.

For an earlier, comprehensive view of the state of the art of standardization the following study is still available:

STANDARDS IN INDUSTRY. Annals of the American Academy of Political and Social Science 137: 1-282, May 1928.
Part I deals with standardization programs in industry and includes papers on the importance of standardization to the economic life of the country; effect of standardization programs on labor, and the contribution of specific groups to particular types of standards. Part II presents papers on aspects of and progress in standardization in various industries and in several manufacturing plants. Part III considers the role of standardization in government, of farm products, in the household, in waste eliminiation, and of hospital supplies. Part IV discusses standardization and its effects on the ultimate consumer.

Hance, Kenneth G. ASSOCIATION MANAGEMENT. Washington, D.C.: Chamber of Commerce of the United States, 1958. 408 p.
The then-chairman of the American Standards Association's Standards Council contributed a chapter on technical research and standardization applicable to the work of an association, together with a detailed discussion of the development, promotion, and establishment of standards.

Now in its third edition is a 42-page STANDARDIZATION MANUAL prepared by the National Association of Purchasing Agents. It discusses in concise form the principles and practices of standardization, and though aimed at an audience of purchasing personnel is equally useful to anyone seeking to orient himself in the field of company standardization.

The following report discusses characteristics of standards and their implications, types of standards, establishing authorities, purposes of standards, their cost, effects on design, production, logistics and training:

Rand Corporation, Santa Monica, California. STANDARDS, STANDARDIZATION AND TEST EQUIPMENT. AD 432 328. Washington, D.C.: U.S. Office of Technical Services, 1960. 27 p.

Reck, Dickson, ed. NATIONAL STANDARDS IN MODERN ECONOMY. New York: Harper, 1956. 372 p.
Available from the American Standards Association, this publication consists of thirty-three papers by various experts who present factual accounts of the standards movement, its history, national and international aspects, effect of the application of standards in government and in industry, implications of the use of national standards with specific reference to product differentiation, resource conservation, automation, and international relations.

Starr, T. H. THE SPECIFICATION AND MANAGEMENT OF MATERIALS IN INDUSTRY. London: Thomas & Hodson, Ltd. 184 p.
Discusses the organization, use and control of standards departments for individual companies.

Easterfield, T. E. STANDARDIZATION AS AN AID TO PRODUCTIVITY. Special Number of Productivity Measurement Review, June 1962. 79 p. Washington, D.C.: Organization for Economic Co-Operation and Development.

Asian Productivity Organization. STANDARDIZATION AND QUALITY CONTROL. Tokyo: Asian Productivity Organization, 1963. 100 p.
Report by a study mission of the APO on standardization and quality control in the United States, the United Kingdom, The Netherlands, West Germany, France, the Republic of China, and Japan. The standardizing bodies in each of the countries are described as well as standards programs in several industrial and manufacturing plants.

U.S. National Bureau of Standards. PROCEEDINGS OF THE 1962 STANDARDS LABORATORY CONFERENCE. Miscellaneous Publication 248. Washington, D.C.: Government Printing Office, 1963. 254 p.

A first conference. The papers presented at the nine sessions include nine on the subject of National Bureau of Standards service to industry; three on measurement standards programs in companies; two on measurement agreement comparisons among standardizing laboratories; and eight on training of measurement personnel.

Shewart, W. A. NATURE AND ORIGIN OF STANDARDS OF QUALITY. Bell System Technical Journal 37:1-22, January 1958.

"This paper discusses the importance, from the viewpoint of judging quality, of: the end to be served by a standard of quality; the nature of the accepted binding force of the standard upon the acts of those interested in the standard; and the role of the judge of quality in shaping the standard in terms of natural law, authority, specification, custom, and precedent."

British Standards Institution. THE OPERATION OF A COMPANY STANDARDS DEPARTMENT. PD 3542. London: British Standards Institution, 1959. 18 p. + 3-page supplement.

Available from the American Standards Association, this document discusses the procedures for setting up and operating a company standards department.

Association Francaise de Normalisation. NOTES FOR THE STANDARDS ENGINEER IN INDUSTRY. Paris: Association Francaise de Normalisation, 1958. 349 p.

An introduction to company standards and standardization for the engineer. Emphasizes basic principles and procedures, and the team concept. Cites many instances of economies effected through simplification and standardization in French and American companies. A very useful appendix includes information on AFNOR regulations and procedures, procedures of the International Organization for Standardization, a suggested numbering system for company standards, and a bibliography. The text is in French, but the six chapters, not including appendix, were translated in issues of Standards Engineering magazine beginning in 1959 and ending in 1961.

Brady, Robert A. ORGANIZATION, AUTOMATION, AND SOCIETY. Berkeley & Los Angeles: University of California Press, 1961. 481 p.

Chapter IV, pp. 108-142, discusses the strategic role of standards between order and innovation. Consumer goods standards and other aspects of standardization are discussed throughout the volume.

Villarroel, Eduardo A. P. THE ROLE OF STANDARDS, CODES AND SPECIFICATIONS IN A MODERN NAVY. Master's Thesis. Monterey, California, U.S. Naval Postgraduate School, 1962. 110 p.

Much of the thesis occupies itself with a review of standardization in general, national and international standardization, standards activity in the United States and Chile. The bibliography contains 76 references, most of which are to the Proceedings of the American Standards Association and the Magazine of Standards.

Milek, John T. STANDARDS AND SPECIFICATIONS DOCUMENTATION SYMBOLS AND ABBREVIATIONS. Los Angeles, California: Standards Press, 1961. 10 p.

A guide to the maze of symbols and abbreviations used by standardizing bodies throughout the world.

Arnell, Alvin. STANDARD GRAPHICAL SYMBOLS. New York, McGraw-Hill, 1963. 534 p.

Symbols used in a broad variety of technical fields and taken directly from established technical standards.

Kinzel, Augustus B. SPECIFICATIONS!?. H. W. Gillett Memorial Lecture, 64th Annual Meeting, American Society for Testing & Materials. Philadelphia: American Society for Testing & Materials, 1961. 12 p.

Reviews the nature, content, use and improvement of specifications, the need for precision, provision for variance, and the development of nondestructive testing techniques.

Vvedenskii, T. A. STANDARDIZATION IN MECHANICAL ENGINEERING. Translated from Russian. Published for the National Science Foundation and the Department of Commerce by the Israel Program for Scientific Translations. Washington, D.C.: U.S. Office of Technical Services, 1962. 56 p. OTS 61-31197.

"Besides discussing the national standards system, including administrative agencies, the work also discusses the organization of standardization within an enterprise, the standardization of the basic products within an enterprise, including technical equipment and standardization sheets. An appendix presents a typical set of regulations for standardization of equipment within an enterprise. Several specific examples of actual national and local standards are also presented in the text."

Farris, Paul L. UNIFORM GRADES AND STANDARDS, PRODUCT DIFFERENTIATION AND PRODUCT DEVELOPMENT. Journal of Farm Economics 42:854-863, November 1960.
The economics of uniform grades and standards, of product differentiation, the complementary relationships between them, and implications for public policy are discussed.

Perry, John. THE STORY OF STANDARDS. New York: Funk & Wagnalls Co. 1955. 271 p.
A history of standards with emphasis on weights and measures and the National Bureau of Standards.

Coles, Jessie V. STANDARDS AND LABELS FOR CONSUMER GOODS. 3rd edition New York: Ronald, 1949. 556 p.
Reviews the basic concepts of standardization; discusses derivation and use of standards, grade labeling; the status of standards and labels for foods, clothing and textiles, drugs, cosmetics, furniture, household equipment, and building materials.

A number of pioneering works on standards and standardization were published more than 25 years ago. Some of these earlier texts, including those by R. E. Brady, C. E. Carpenter, A. L. Edwards, N. F. Harriman, and J. G. Gaillard, now out of print, may be located by consulting the CUMULATIVE BOOK INDEX, published by the H. W. Wilson Company, New York.

A descriptive inventory of the work of 350 United States trade associations and technical societies involved in standardization was published as NBS Miscellaneous Publication 230, superseding an earlier, similar compilation:

U.S. National Bureau of Standards. STANDARDIZATION ACTIVITIES IN THE UNITED STATES. Washington, D.C.: Government Printing Office, 1960. 210 p.

A directory-in-the-making was announced in mid-1964 by the National Conference of Standards Laboratories. The forthcoming volume is the DIRECTORY OF STANDARDS LABORATORIES IN THE UNITED STATES, a classified index of standards laboratories in this country. The National Bureau of Standards issued a preliminary edition on October 12, 1964.

The BUILDING SCIENCE DIRECTORY published by the Building Research

Institute, Washington, D.C. lists 947 trade associations, technical societies, government agencies and educational institutions which are associated with the building field, both intimately and peripherally. The organizations reflect technical, construction, regulatory, financial, economic and social interests. 251 of these organizations are described on individual data sheets which list the organization's publications and states the nature of its activity in the area of standards and codes. A looseleaf, subscription service.

Standards-related information is also available in the ENCYCLOPEDIA OF ASSOCIATIONS, 4th edition, published by Gale Research Company. More than 12,500 organizations are listed. Among those listed in Section 1, Trade, Business and Commercial Organizations, and in Section 4, Scientific, Engineering and Technical Organizations, will be found most of the organizations involved in some phase of standards activity. The brief descriptive annotations which accompany the name and address of each association will, if pertinent, contain such phrases as, "Develops and establishes equipment and applications standards," "Prepares standards and codes," "Conducts research programs in such areas as commercial standards and codes relating to . . .". Standards and codes committees and divisions are frequently listed by title.

National Academy of Sciences-National Research Council. SCIENTIFIC AND TECHNICAL SOCIETIES OF THE UNITED STATES AND CANADA. 7th edition. Publication 900. Washington, D.C.: National Academy of Sciences-National Research Council, 1961. 413 + 54 pp + Index.

An alphabetical list of 1836 scientific and technical societies with details on the history, purposes, membership, meetings, professional activities, and publications of each organization. Standardization activities are briefly indicated under statement of purpose or professional activity.

Chamber of Commerce of the United States. 1961 SURVEY OF ASSOCIATION ACTIVITIES AND BUSINESS PROBLEMS. Washington, D.C.: Chamber of Commerce of the United States, 1961. 25 p.

The survey covers 874 national, regional, state and local associations. Of these 275 reported some form of standardization activity. A brief description of these activities is given.

U.S. National Bureau of Standards. DIRECTORY OF COMMITTEE MEMBERSHIPS AND ADVISORY COMMITTEES TO NBS. Washington, D.C.: National Bureau of Standards, 1962. 75 p.

The purpose of this directory is to show the extent and variety of NBS personnel participation in extending assistance in many fields of science and technology by listing, alphabetically, the names of technical societies, trade associations, government agencies and other organizations and the names of NBS staff who are members of committees within these various organizations. Since many of these committees have to deal with standards and specifications, this directory becomes a useful source of names of such committees. For example, this directory will tell you that the American Petroleum Institute has a committee on Standardization of Rotary Drilling Equipment Gages and Gaging Practice, that the American Public Health Association has one on Standardization of Radioactivity Methods, and that the American Society of Mechanical Engineers has one on International Standardization.

Among some of the more recent technical journal articles which provide directory information may be cited the following:

Leerburger, B. A., Jr. SOCIETIES AND ASSOCIATIONS OFFERING DESIGN DATA AND STANDARDS. Product Engineering 31:55-60, February 8, 1960.

Indicates for 93 trade associations and technical societies whether they publish standards other than those listed by the American Standards Association.

Kaidanovsky, S. P. GUIDE TO MATERIALS STANDARDS & SPECIFICATIONS. 24 p. Reprint from Materials in Design Engineering, March, April, May, June, July, August 1958 issues.

Describes Federal, Military Commercial, ASTM, SAE, and American Standards. Details are presented on sources for standards and specifications on iron and steels, nonferrous metals, plastics and rubber, nonmetallics, and finishes and coatings.

Kaidanovsky, S. P. SOURCES OF INFORMATION FOR STANDARDS GOVERNMENT, NATIONAL, AND OTHER STANDARDS. Proceedings of the Standards Engineers Society, 1957. pp. 27-37.

Discusses the work of some of the more outstanding technical organizations in the field of engineering materials standards.

Gorn, S., editor. STRUCTURES OF STANDARD-PROCESSING ORGANIZATIONS IN THE COMPUTER AREA. Communications of the ACM 6:294-305, June 1963.

Discussed in detail is the work of the International Organization for Standardization, the International Electrotechnical Commission, the European Computer Manufacturers Association, the International Federation for Information Processing, the American Standards Association.

Also covering the computer field is the following:

PRIMER ON STANDARDS AND THE GROUPS PROPOSING THEM (FOR INFORMATION PROCESSING). Computation & Automation 12:13-15, July 1963.

Preuss, H. P. SOURCES FOR OFFICIAL PAINT SPECIFICATIONS AND TESTING RPOCEDURES. Metal Finishing 60:78-80, June 1962.

Lists sources for Military and Federal Specifications, and the standards available from seven trade and technical societies and several Federal Government agencies.

Very frequently textbooks and handbooks in materials engineering and technology as well as in other technical areas include a chapter or section dealing with standards organizations or standards and codes. No attempt has been made to compile a list of such references. The descriptive annotations which appear in the catalogs of technical and scientific publishers do usually indicate whether the book contains such information.

Company programs and practices in standardization were surveyed in the National Industrial Conference Board's INDUSTRIAL STANDARDIZATION (Studies in Business Policy, No. 85), revised in 1957. 71 p.

The following basic treatise on standardization was recently translated into English:

Wodzicki, Jan. STANDARDIZATION--BASIC INFORMATION. TT-62-11067N. Springfield, Va., Clearinghouse for Federal Scientific and Technical Information (successor organization to the Office of Technical Services), 1964. 79 p.

"The author says that standardization is generally considered from the point of view of standards; it should be perceived and studied from the point of view of life. He gives examples from nature, and discusses standardization as a factor which facilitates living, spreads culture and develops security and safety."

Section 2

BIBLIOGRAPHIES, AND INDEXES TO PERIODICALS

Section 2

BIBLIOGRAPHIES, AND INDEXES TO PERIODICALS

If the field of standardization is somewhat underprivileged for lack of a handbook, it is no less underprivileged for lack of a comprehensive bibliography of the literature of standardization. Several thousand journal articles, documents, and books have appeared in print during the past five years, but the most recent, considerably-less-than-comprehensive bibliography is the following:

LITERATURE RECOMMENDATIONS: STANDARDIZATION. Washington, D.C.: International Cooperation Administration, 1959. 76 p.

About 450 references covering the period 1946-1956 are included in this bibliography prepared by the John Crerar Library under contract to the Office of Technical Services. General aspects of standardization; international, governmental, and society activities; company programs, legal aspects; and references to various fields of application are listed.

References to the literature prior to 1940 appear in:

U.S. National Bureau of Standards. STANDARDIZATION ACTIVITIES OF NATIONAL TECHNICAL AND TRADE ASSOCIATIONS. Miscellaneous Publication M169. Washington, D.C.: Government Printing Office, 1941. 288 p.

Section V of this manual, pp. 243-265 consists of a Bibliography of the Library of Congress which also prepared bibliographies on standardization appearing in National Bureau of Standards' Standard Yearbooks for the years 1928, 1929, 1930, and 1933, and in Miscellaneous Publication No. 136 of the NBS.

BIBLIOGRAPHIES, AND INDEXES TO PERIODICALS

From time to time are published bibliographies on standards in special fields. Attention has already been called to the measurement standards bibliography which accompanies Section 5.4 of the handbook under preparation by the Standards Engineers Society. Others are:

Milek, J. T. and Eccleston, Evelyn. A BIBLIOGRAPHY ON STANDARDIZATION IN THE CERAMICS INDUSTRY. Los Angeles: Standards Press, 1961. 14 p.

BIBLIOGRAPHY OF MEASUREMENT STANDARDS. ISA Journal 8:71-4, February 1961.
A compilation of 175 references by the Instrument Society of America Measurement Standards Division and the National Bureau of Standards. 43 National Bureau of Standards publications are included.

Wuster, Eugen. BIBLIOGRAPHY OF MONOLINGUAL, SCIENTIFIC AND TECHNICAL GLOSSARIES. Volume 1. National Standards. 219 p. Volume 2. Miscellaneous Sources. 146 p. Paris: United Nations Educational, Scientific and Cultural Organization, 1955-1959.
Essentially a catalog of lists of technical terms pertaining to various fields of knowledge and published in one language. Arranged according to the Universal Decimal Classification. Within each subject group the glossaries are arranged in alphabetical order under the language to which they belong. Contains subject, language and organizations indexes, and the names and addresses of the standardizing bodies which issue the glossaries listed in Volume 1.

U.S. Atomic Energy Commission. RADIATION PROTECTION STANDARDS. A LITERATURE SEARCH, compiled by William E. Bost. TID-3551 Washington, D.C.: U.S. Office of Technical Services, 1960. 28 p.
538 references to reports, journal articles and books published 1957-1959.

U.S. Atomic Energy Commission. THE EFFECTS OF RADIATION AND RADIOISOTOPES ON THE LIFE PROCESSES; AN ANNOTATED BIBLIOGRAPHY. Book 1. TID-3098. Washington, D.C.: U.S. Office of Technical Services, 1963. 736 p.
Fifty-five references to documents and journals on the subject of radiation standards are included in pp.99-106.

BIBLIOGRAPHIE DER NORMEN (BIBLIOGRAPHY OF STANDARDS ON DOCUMENTATION). FID Publication 303. The Hague: Federation Internationale de Documentaion, 1958.

Available from the American Standards Association.

ENGINEERED PERFORMANCE STANDARDS. SB-514. Washington, D.C.: U.S. Office of Technical Services, 1964. 3 p.

List of 29 U.S. Navy, Bureau of Yards and Docks standards added to the OTS collection through April, 1964.

Rossnagel, W. B. A GUIDE TO GOVERNMENTAL ASSURANCE DOCUMENTATION. Machine Design 36:157-161, April 9, 1964.

An excellent guide to the basic documents in the fields of reliability, quality assurance, maintainability, value analysis, safety, and human factors. In addition to manuals, regulations, letters, and bulletins, general military standards, design specifications and lists of specifications are included. Examples of the latter are NAVWEPS 00-25-544, LIST OF SPECIFICATIONS AND STANDARDS APPROVED BY BUWEPS, and NAVWEPS 00-25-543, LIST OF STANDARDS DRAWINGS USED BY BUWEPS.

BIBLIOGRAPHY ON HOUSING, BUILDING AND PLANNING. Washington, D.C.: U.S. Housing and Home Finance Agency, 1964. 52 p.

"Building Codes and Standards," pp. 3-4. The 23 references include building codes issued by trade associations and technical societies.

U. S. Housing and Home Finance Agency. HOUSING AND PLANNING REFERENCES. Washington, D.C.: U.S. Housing and Home Finance Agency.

A bi-monthly bibliography of selected publications added to the library of the Agency. The subject headings "Building Codes and Standards," "Modular Coordination," and "Standards and Specifications" should be checked for pertinent books and articles.

Joy, Barbara Ellen. ANNOTATED BIBLIOGRAPHY ON CAMPING. Minneapolis: Burgess Publishing Co., 1962. 126 p.

20 standards publications issued by the American Camping Association and other organizations.

Aronson, M. H., ed. HANDBOOK OF ELECTRICAL MEASUREMENTS. Pittsburgh: Instruments Publishing Co., 1963. 84 p.

21 authors contributed 24 articles on equipment for a standards laboratory; setting up a standardization laboratory; local standards laboratories; and the electrical standards laboratory. Existing practices in several companies are described.

Milek, J. T. WRITING SPECIFICATIONS: A TEACHING UNIT OF INSTRUCTION. Standards Engineering 15:3-6, December 1963.

In this presentation of material actually used as a unit of instruction in a 3-hour class on Specifications Writing, the author includes a brief description of guides, surveys and sources of information and a bibliography of 55 references on standards and specifications dealing with ferrous and nonferrous materials, heat treating and metal finishing, and miscellaneous standards and specifications on metals.

SCIENTIFIC TESTS, STANDARDS. Price List 64. Washington, D.C.: Government Printing Office, 1963. 22 p.

A selected list of Government publications in print. Included are Standards Handbooks and Monographs issued by the National Bureau of Standards, a list of Commercial Standards and Simplified Practice Recommendations, and documents dealing with calibration and weights and measures. Other Price Lists likely to contain the titles of publications dealing with standards are Price List 10, LAWS, RULES, AND REGULATIONS, and Price List 11, HOME ECONOMICS, FOODS AND COOKING.

American Conference of Governmental Industrial Hygienists. SELECTED BIBLIOGRAPHY OF RADIATION PROTECTION ORGANIZATIONS. Cincinnati: American Conference of Governmental Industrial Hygienists, 1963. 106 p..

A descriptive list of international, national advisory, and governmental organizations, and societies and associations whose activities relate to radiation protection. Incorporated in each description is a list of some of the more important reports issued, many of which deal with radiation standards.

"Recent Publications on Standardization" is the title of a feature which appears fairly regularly in STANDARDS ENGINEERING, monthly journal of the Standards Engineers Society. New standards and new books are listed as well as selected articles from technical and trade journals.

The MONTHLY CATALOG, UNITED STATES GOVERNMENT PUBLICA-

TIONS is issued monthly by the Government Printing Office. Standards publications emanating from the various Federal agencies are included along with most other Government publications. The subject index heading "Standards and Standardization" will serve as a guide to some publications, but specific subjects must be checked in order to locate all publications listed in an issue. An annual index appears in December issues.

Two other journals available from the Government Printing Office abstract and index standards documents, respectively. One is NUCLEAR SCIENCE ABSTRACTS, prepared by the Division of Technical Information, U.S. Atomic Energy Commission, and issued bi-monthly. Indexes appear in each issue as well as semi-annually and annually. Recent annual indexes have listed, under the subject heading "Standards," thirty to forty documents on standards and specifications in the field of nuclear science. The other journal, also issued twice a month, is U.S. GOVERNMENT RESEARCH REPORTS, issued by the U.S. Office of Technical Services. Its purpose is to announce new reports of research and development released by the Army, Navy, Air Force, Atomic Energy Commission, and other agencies of the Federal Government. An illustrative list of publications on standards and standardization which were announced in recent issues follows:

AD 602 047 STANDARDIZATION ENGINEERING PRACTICES STUDY OF ELECTRONIC COMPONENT PARTS.

AD 435 843 STANDARD PROCEDURE FOR USING UNITS OF MASS, WEIGHT, FORCE, PRESSURE AND ACCELERATION.

PB 158 305 IRIG TELEMETRY STANDARDS

PB 181 389 FREQUENCY STANDARDS AND MEASUREMENTS

PB 181 605 STANDARDS FOR DESCRIPTIVE CATALOGING OF GOVERNMENT SCIENTIFIC AND TECHNICAL REPORTS

AD 272 600 STANDARDIZED UNIVERSAL TOOLING PROGRAM

AD 288 914 DESIGN MODIFICATIONS AND 1962 COST ANALYSIS FOR A STANDARDIZED SERIES OF FALLOUT SHELTERS

AD 274 545 DEVELOPMENT OF A STANDARD COMMUNICATION RATING SYSTEM

PB 155 961 OPTIMIZATION AND STANDARDIZATION OF INFORMATION RETRIEVAL LANGUAGE AND SYSTEM

AD 432 328 STANDARDS, STANDARDIZATION AND TEST EQUIPMENT

The Air Pollution Control Association, in cooperation with the U.S. Public Health Service, and the Library of Congress, publishes the monthly APCA ABSTRACTS. Abstracts are listed numerically under twelve broad categories, one of which is Books, Manuals, Selected Publications, Specifications, Standards, Technical Reports. A cumulative subject index is part of the July issue, the most recent of which (1964) indexed 43 references on standards and specifications relating to air quality and air pollution.

Several indexes to periodicals are essential tools for locating the literature on standardization:

APPLIED SCIENCE & TECHNOLOGY INDEX. New York: H. W. Wilson Company, 1958 to date.

A successor to The Industrial Arts Index (1913-1957), this is a cumulative subject index to 200 periodicals in the fields of aeronautics, automation, chemistry, construction, electricity and electrical communication, engineering, geology and metallurgy, industrial and mechanical arts, machinery, physics, and transportation. Articles are indexed under, e.g.,

Standardization
Standards
Standards, International
Specifications
Electric Standards
Safety Standards

and the subdivision Standards under special subjects, e.g., Automobile engineering-Standards.

The H. W. Wilson Company also publishes BUSINESS PERIODICALS INDEX, 1958 to date and AGRICULTURAL INDEX, 1916 to date. The latter has been renamed BIOLOGY & AGRICULTURAL INDEX beginning with the October 1964 number. The former indexes a broad range of trade journals which frequently carry articles on standards and specifications. The latter is especially useful for locating articles dealing with food standards and standards for farm machinery.

Engineering Index, Inc. publishes a monthly abstract bulletin entitled

ENGINEERING INDEX. Articles for inclusion are selected from 1000 periodicals, serial publications, conference papers and symposia as well as from other non-serial publications "on the basis of engineering significance." References to articles on standards are found under the specific subject to which they apply. Relatively little material is listed under the subject headings "Standards" and "Standardization." The Engineering Index also publishes an annual volume and an Engineering Index Card Service.

A built-in library of the literature of standardization would incorporate complete sets of the PROCEEDINGS OF THE NATIONAL CONFERENCES ON STANDARDS, 1950 to date, issued by the American Standards Association, and PROCEEDINGS of the annual meetings of the Standards Engineers Society, 1952 to date. On the average, some two dozen papers on various phases of standardization have been presented at each conference.

Because there appears to be a revival of interest in standards for consumer goods, some of the literature of the 1920s and 1930s on this aspect of standardization is worthy of note.

Mann, George C. BIBLIOGRAPHY ON CONSUMER EDUCATION. New York: Harper, 1939. 286 p.
Chapter IV, Standards, Labels and Consumer Protection cites over 125 book and periodical references. An even more extensive bibliography is appended to:

Coles, Jessie V. STANDARDIZATION OF CONSUMERS' GOODS. New York: Ronald, 1932. 312 p.
General works as well as more specific references on the status of standards on drugs, equipment and furnishings, food products, textiles and clothing, and weights and measures are included in pp. 299-312.

The forthcoming 1965 National Conference on Standards sponsored by the American Standards Association has as its theme, "Standards and the Consumer." The published proceedings available in mid-1965, will reflect the views of industry, government, and consumer spokesmen on the future course of consumer standards, both national and international.

Another expected publication will be a report of an ad hoc committee of the American Society for Testing and Materials appointed in September 1964 for the purpose of studying the problem of ASTM's future contribution to the development of standards for consumer goods. In considering the role of ASTM in writing consumer standards, the Society's president suggested that the ASTM was probably in the best position to undertake this difficult job.[1]

Food products represent an area in which standards and grades of some benefit to consumers have been in existence for several decades. Many articles dealing with grading, inspection, quality, and standardization of fresh and processed foods are indexed in the BIBLIOGRAPHY OF AGRICULTURE, prepared by the National Agricultural Library, U.S. Department of Agriculture. Washington, D.C.: Government Printing Office. Monthly.

1. Williams, I.V. ASTM--STATICS AND DYNAMICS. MATERIALS RESEARCH & STANDARDS 4:440-441, August 1964.

Section 3

CATALOGS AND INDEXES OF STANDARDS AND SPECIFICATIONS, AND COMPILATIONS OF STANDARDS AND SPECIFICATIONS

Section 3

CATALOGS AND INDEXES OF STANDARDS AND SPECIFICATIONS, AND COMPILATIONS OF STANDARDS AND SPECIFICATIONS

Forty years ago the National Bureau of Standards undertook to publish the first edition of the NATIONAL DIRECTORY OF COMMODITY SPECIFICATIONS. It was a classified, annotated list of all commodity standards and specifications issued by over 300 associations, societies and government agencies. This monumental task was discontinued in 1947 when a supplement to the 1300-page third edition was issued.

In the intervening years there have been sporadic mutterings about the possibility of a revival of this publication under different auspices, but at least 350 organizations are now too busy grinding out commodity standards and specifications to give much thought to the need for recording, in an orderly fashion, what everyone is doing. Anyone seeking to obtain a comprehensive view of the standards and specifications available in this country would have to consult guides listed in this section and the list of association publications recorded in Section 5.

American Standards Association. 1964 CATALOG OF AMERICAN STANDARDS. New York: American Standards Association, 1964. 74 p.

An annual price list of American Standards current as of December 31st of the year preceding publication date. The 1964 catalog lists 2250 standards under 23 major project areas and 450 subdivisions. Standards are listed according to ASA-number designations, with an appended title index. Other features of the catalog are separate lists of American Safety Standards, American Standards for Consumer Goods, International Organization for Standardization Recommendations, International Commission Recommendations, and Specifications of the International Commission on Rules for the Approval of Electrical Equipment. There is also an Organizational Cross Index which provides lists of American Standards that also carry the designations of other organizations.

American Society for Testing and Materials. INDEX TO STANDARDS. Philadelphia, American Society for Testing and Materials, 1964.
Issued annually. An index to over 1800 Standards and Tentative Standards published by the Society. Standards comprise the specifications and methods of test formally adopted by the Society. Tentatives represent the latest thoughts and practices on the subject covered. The index also has a subject and numerical list of Standards and Tentatives. The ASTM's compilations of Standards are described in Section 5.

There are two major indexes to United States Government standards and specifications:

General Services Administration. Federal Supply Service, INDEX OF FEDERAL SPECIFICATIONS AND STANDARDS. Washington, D.C.: Government Printing Office, 1964.
Issued annually on January 1, with monthly cumulative supplements. Contains alphabetical key word and numerical group listing of Federal Specifications, Federal Standards, Federal Handbooks, General Services Administration Specifications, and those Military Specifications and Standards which may be used by all Federal agencies in their purchasing. More than 4,000 documents are included.

U.S. Department of Defense. Defense Supply Agency. INDEX OF SPECIFICATIONS AND STANDARDS. Washington, D.C.: Government Printing Office, 1964.
The basic volumes are issued annually in July with cumulative supplements appearing every two months. Listed are Military, Federal, and Departmental specifications, standards, handbooks and related standardization documents used by the Department of Defense and its various subdivisions in procurement. Part I is an alphabetical listing. Part II is a numerical listing. Part III is a listing by Federal Supply Classification numbers. The combined parts run to some 4,000 pages.

Air World Publications. MILITARY SPECIFICATIONS BUYERS DIRECTORY. Los Angeles: Air World Publications, 1964.
A quarterly-revised listing of Military specifications and

standards, together with all government-approved sources of supply--more than 10,000 manufacturers. Includes alphabetical index of parts and components cross-referenced to applicable military specifications and standards.

U.S. Department of Commerce. COMMERCIAL STANDARDS AND SIMPLIFIED PRACTICE RECOMMENDATIONS. List of Publications 53. Washington, D.C.: U.S. Department of Commerce, 1965. 16 p.

Lists about 500 voluntary industry standards issued under the aegis of the Department's Office of Commodity Standards.

U.S. Department of Agriculture. CHECKLIST OF U.S. STANDARDS FOR FARM PRODUCTS. AMS-210 (Revised). Washington, D.C.: U.S. Department of Agriculture, 1964. 16 p.

Lists all of the 350 or more standards developed and issued by the seven commodity divisions of the Agricultural Marketing Service--Cotton, Dairy, Fruit and Vegetable, Grain, Livestock, Poultry, and Tobacco. Also briefly describes the ten acts of Congress making standards mandatory under certain conditions. A list of sixteen U.S.D.A. publications dealing with some aspect of standardization and grading is part of this Checklist.

Instrument Society of America. STANDARDS AND PRACTICES FOR INSTRUMENTATION. Pittsburgh: Instrument Society of America, 1963.

In addition to reproducing every standard and recommended practice of the ISA in full, this compilation contains abstracts of more than 300 instrumentation and automatic control standards developed by 19 technical societies and trade associations, and lists of British and Canadian Instrumentation standards.

Gunderson, Frank L., Gunderson, Helen W., and Ferguson, Egbert R., Jr. FOOD STANDARDS AND DEFINITIONS IN THE UNITED STATES: A GUIDEBOOK. New York: Academic Press, 1963. 269 p.

Lists and describes food standards established by acts of the U.S. Congress, by the Food and Drug Administration, the Agricultural Research Service, the Agricultural Marketing Service, the Bureau of Commercial Fisheries, the Treasury Department, the Department of Commerce, the Federal Trade Commission, the Veterans Administration, and the General Services Administration. There is also a description of principal periodical publications on Food Standards in the United States. An appendix of 100 pages consists of photocopies of typical standards as cited and discussed in the text.

Emerick, Robert H. HEATING HANDBOOK: A MANUAL OF STANDARDS, CODES, AND METHODS. New York: McGraw-Hill, 1964. 522 p.

"This handbook is planned to make available to the heating engineer, the specification writer, the architect, and to contractors working in the heating field, guiding information on related codes and standards." The 28 sections into which the book is divided make reference to and quote applicable sections of the standards and codes of 54 technical societies, trade associations, and government agencies. The introductory chapter discusses the nature of codes, standards and procedures and lists the names of and addresses of the standardizing bodies.

American Standards Association. CATALOG OF SELECTED FOREIGN ELECTRICAL STANDARDS. New York: American Standards Association, 1962. 200 p. O.P.

List of the national electrical standards issued by 38 countries. The standards for each country are listed under 27 broad subject categories, e.g., Batteries and Cells, Control Equipment, Domestic Appliances, Motors and Generators.

American Society of Heating, Refrigerating and Air-Conditioning Engineers. ASHRAE GUIDE AND DATA BOOK. FUNDAMENTALS AND EQUIPMENT. New York: American Society of Heating, Refrigerating and Air-Conditioning Engineers, 1963.

Chapter 67, entitled Codes and Standards, provides an alphabetical subject listing of the 200 standards and codes issued by 60 organizations on matters dealing with air-conditioning, heating and refrigeration.

Reinhart, F. W. FEDERAL TEST METHODS STANDARDS. SPE Journal 17:1291-1297, December 1961.

Lists of Federal and Military Specifications and Commercial Standards for plastics and plastic products.

The following publications, all available from the U.S. Office of Technical Services also deal with plastics:

AD 410 401 GOVERNMENT SPECIFICATIONS AND STANDARDS FOR PLASTICS COVERING DEFENSE ENGINEERING MATERIALS AND APPLICATIONS, 1963. 62 p.

AD 402 225 DEFENSE SPECIFICATIONS AND STANDARDS FOR AND RELATING TO REINFORCED PLASTICS, 1963. 11 p.

PB 171 038 GUIDE TO SPECIFICATIONS FOR RIGID LAMINATED PLASTICS, 1962. 359 p.

Cement Statistical and Technical Association. REVIEW OF THE PORTLAND CEMENT STANDARDS OF THE WORLD. Malmo, Sweden: Cement Statistical and Technical Association, 1961. 96 p.
Describes standards in the 42 countries which have issued their own national specifications. Chemical, physical and strength requirements of each country are reviewed.

SPECIFICATIONS FOR PORTLAND CEMENT. Cement & Lime Manufacture (London) 35:35-44, May; 61-67, July 1962.
The two articles present tabular information from the Portland cement specifications of various countries. The May article gives data relating to chemical composition, setting time and soundness. The July article gives strength requirements.

Commerce Clearing House. FOOD DRUG COSMETIC LAW REPORTER. Chicago; Commerce Clearing House, 1963 to date. 4 volumes.
Looseleaf service. The volume devoted to Food includes texts of the Standards of Identity promulgated by the U.S. Food and Drug Administration, and a list of food commodity Grade Standards of the Agricultural Marketing Service, U.S. Department of Agriculture.

THE ALMANAC OF THE CANNING, FREEZING, PRESERVING INDUSTRIES. Westminster, Maryland: E. E. Judge Publisher, 1964. 478 p. Annual.
Section III Food & Drug Standards of Identity, Quality and Fill. pp. 78-170.
Section IV USDA Quality Grade Standards, Canned, Glass & Frozen. pp. 171-283.
These are texts of the standards issued by the two government agencies. Also, on pp. 284-286, the text of State of Maine Grades for Sardines in Oil are given.

U. S. Bureau of Labor Standards. FEDERAL SAFETY COUNCIL DIGEST OF RECOMMENDED SAFETY STANDARDS, SAFE PRACTICES AND GUIDES. Washington, D.C.: U.S. Bureau of Labor Standards, n.d. 38 p.
The safety standards and guides of 17 government and

non-government organizations are excerpted under the following categories: organization and administration; physical; environmental; mechanical; chemical; and motor vehicle.

National Association of State Purchasing Officials. INDEX OF STATE SPECIFICATIONS OF COMMODITIES, 1963. Chicago: The Council of State Governments, 1963. 79 p.
An alphabetical listing of more than 1300 commodities taken from the 1963 Index of Federal Specifications. For each commodity is indicated the type of specification--Federal or State--which is being used by specific States. The listing serves to identify commodities for which individual states have issued their own standards.

National Paint, Varnish and Lacquer Association. GUIDE TO UNITED STATES GOVERNMENT PAINT SPECIFICATIONS. 16th edition. Washington, D.C.: National Paint, Varnish and Lacquer Association, 1961 to date. 309 p.
Compilation of abstracts presenting essential data from the numerous paint specifications issued by government agencies. Included are Federal and Military Specifications and those issued by the U.S. Bureau of Reclamation, the Maritime Administration, the Tennessee Valley Authority, the Association of State Highway Officials, and those emanating from Committee D-1 of the American Society for Testing and Materials. The basic editions are kept current by frequent supplements.

National Microfilm Association. BASIC DOD SPECIFICATIONS AND STANDARDS. NMA Informational Monograph No. 1. Annapolis: National Microfilm Association, 1963. 168 p.
Facsimile reprints of basic Department of Defense Specifications and standards which are in effect for contract and other microfilm work undertaken by the Department.

Association of Casualty and Surety Companies. HANDBOOK OF INDUSTRIAL SAFETY STANDARDS. New York: Association of Casualty and Surety Companies, 1962. 315 p.
Compilation of industrial safety requirements based on codes and recommendations of the American Standards Association, the National Fire Protection Association, the American Society of Mechanical Engineers and several government agencies.

American Welding Society. INDEX OF WELDING STANDARDS FROM 21 NATIONS. New York: American Welding Society,

1962. 144 p.
The standards of each country are separately classified in French, English, and the original language. Address sources for the standards are given.

National Aerospace Standards Committee. NATIONAL AEROSPACE STANDARDS ALPHABETICAL AND NUMERICAL INDEXES. Washington, D.C.: Aerospace Industries Association of America, 1964.
Lists of approximately 1000 standards covering machinery, assemblies, parts, components, measurements, and procedures. Published and distributed by the National Standards Association, Washington, D.C.

Society of Automotive Engineers. SAE HANDBOOK. New York: Society of Automotive Engineers, 1964.
Annual publication which runs close to 1000 pages and is a compilation of SAE Standards, Information Reports and Recommended Practices. There is also a considerable amount of information concerning other SAE publications, officers, boards, committees, rules and regulations, and other organizational information.

Society of Automotive Engineers. AMS INDEX. New York: Society of Automotive Engineers, 1964.
Lists more than 1000 SAE Aerospace Materials Specifications for accessories, fabricated parts and assemblies; ferrous and non-ferrous alloys; refractory and refractive materials; tolerances; quality control, and many others.

Society of Automotive Engineers. AS, ARP, AIR INDEX. New York: Society of Automotive Engineers, 1964.
A list of 330 SAE Aerospace Standards, Aerospace Recommended Practices, and Aerospace Information Reports. Aerospace Standards are design or part standards applicable to missile, airframe, ground support equipment; propulsion, propeller and accessory equipment, and airline industries. ARPs give dimensional, design or performance recommendations intended as guides for standards engineering practice. AIRs contain engineering data and general information useful to aerospace industries.

U.S. Department of Defense. CROSS-INDEX OF CHEMICALLY EQUIVALENT SPECIFICATIONS AND IDENTIFICATION CODE (FERROUS AND NONFERROUS ALLOYS). MIL-Handbook-H 1B. Washington, D.C.: Government Printing Office, 1958. 366 p.

Provides a single five-digit code number for ferrous and nonferrous alloys of similar composition for which there are specifications from many sources.

Defense Fuel Supply Center, Washington, D.C. REFERENCE LIST OF SPECIFICATIONS AND STANDARDS FOR PETROLEUM AND RELATED PRODUCTS. AD 436 434. Washington, D.C.: U.S. Office of Technical Services, 1964. 45 p.

Stern, A. C. SUMMARY OF EXISTING AIR POLLUTION STANDARDS. Journal of the Air Pollution Control Association 14:5-15, January 1964.

A tabular summary of existing ambient air quality and emission standards published in the United States and abroad. Discusses procedures for setting air quality standards and formulating specifications.

Barnecut, R. J. APPLICABLE CODES AND REQUIREMENTS. Air Conditioning, Heating and Ventilating 61:64-69, July 1964.

Lists and discusses pertinent building, safety, fire, plumbing and other codes applicable to hospital construction and gives sources for the various documents.

Joint Industry Conference. JIC ELECTRICAL STANDARDS AND INDUSTRIAL EQUIPMENT. Electro-Technology, June 1957. Reprint. 24 p.

This informal industry group also promulgated Hydraulic and Pneumatic Standards.

Yeaple, Franklin D. WHAT WILL HAPPEN TO JIC ELECTRICAL STANDARDS? Product Engineering 34:63-67, March 4, 1963.

In discussing the need for and problems involved in devising a single-industry-wide electrical standard based on JIC, the author describes features of electrical standards of the American Standards Association, the Industrial Electrical Equipment Council (supersedes JIC), the National Electrical Manufacturers Association, the National Machine Tool Builders Association, and the National Fire Protection Association.

Demarest, William. BUILDING CODES: PRODUCT APPROVALS PREPARED FOR THE PLASTICS GROUP OF THE MANUFACTURING CHEMISTS ASSOCIATION. New Haven, Connecticut: Ludlow-Bookman, 1964. 63 p.

Guide for the building product manufacturer who needs building code recognition of his product. It is both a primer on the workings of the code-making bodies and a reference book giving specific requirements of major representative city, state and Federal regulatory authorities.

Naval Boiler and Turbine Laboratory, Philadelphia, Pa. INSTRUMENT STANDARDS. 11th ed. AD 602 036. Washington, D.C.: U.S. Office of Technical Services, 1964. 305 p.

"The Standard Plans contained in this binder constitute Naval Boiler and Turbine Laboratory Instrument Practice as of the date of issue...They represent only repetitive items; each test measurement system is designed according to its own requirements, the standards being used where applicable." Beginning with this edition the Standards on Flow measurement have been removed from this volume and are being issued as a separate publication.

David Taylor Model Basin, Washington, D.C. STANDARDIZATION REQUIREMENTS FOR TECHNICAL REPORTS. Revision No. 2. AD 601 706. Washington, D.C.: U.S. Office of Technical Services, 1963. 44 p.

"The report presents the technical report standards by the Bureau of Ships for its various laboratories and defines the different kinds of BuShips reports. It also outlines the procedures to be followed by the David Taylor Model Basin in the preparation and publication of technical reports consistent with BuShips policy."

Under contract with the U.S. Bureau of Ships the American Standards Association is cross-indexing and analyzing comparable industry and military specifications. These analyses have been reported each month in the American Standards Association's Magazine of Standards, beginning February 1961, in a section entitled "Cross-Indexing Industry and Military Specifications and Standards." The equivalent and divergent areas of comparable standards and specifications are reported.

A compilation of these cross-indexed industry and military standards and specifications is available as Chapter 6 of the U.S. Bureau of Ships STANDARDIZATION MANUAL (NAVSHIPS 250-350). Chapter 6 is entitled, "Cross Index, Industry-Military Specifications & Standards." The issue of August 1961 includes the basic publication of that date plus six quarterly supplements issued subsequently. Supplement No. 7 of Chapter 6 was issued October 1963, Supplement 8 in May 1964, and Supplement 9 in November 1964.

Section 4

GOVERNMENT SOURCES

Section 4

GOVERNMENT SOURCES

The Director of the General Services Administration, purchasing agent for the Federal Government, in commenting upon the existing 3,848 Federal and Interim Federal Specifications and 156 Standards available for use in procurement stated that: "It is estimated that in order to provide for competitive procurement at the lowest total cost 6,700 Federal Specifications together with 5,608 amendments, and 573 Federal Standards with 464 amendments will be required by 1969." These figures are only a partial indication of how deeply the Government is involved in standardization and how deeply it will continue to be involved.

As mentioned earlier, the most recent report on the standardization activities of Federal Government agencies is contained in the CONSUMER STANDARDS monograph prepared by S. P. Kaidanovsky in 1941. For the uninitiated several informative, more recent publications are available.

U.S. General Services Administrative. Federal Supply Service. GUIDE TO SPECIFICATIONS AND STANDARDS OF THE FEDERAL GOVERNMENT. Washington, D.C.: U.S. General Services Administration, 1963. 39 p.

Briefly describes the purpose and kinds of Government standards and specifications, how they are developed and used, how industry participates in their development, and how copies of standards and specifications may be obtained.

Subtitled, "A Guide for Selling or Buying in the Government Market" is another booklet which includes a description of Government standards and specifications, how they are used, and where they may be obtained by prospective bidders. It lists about 1,000 Government activities and depository libraries where specifications and indexes to them are available for reference purposes:

> Small Business Administration. U.S. GOVERNMENT PURCHASING, SPECIFICATIONS AND SALES DIRECTORY. Washington, D.C.: Government Printing Office, 1962. 116 p.

The role of Government in standardization is very frequently the subject of several papers or symposia at annual conferences of technical societies and trade associations. The frequency with which the names of certain Federal officials appear on such programs might lead one to believe that an inordinate amount of time must be spent by them or their assistants in preparing and presenting their talks. However, as is typical of frequently-called-upon speakers, they have learned to economize by presenting appropriately revised and re-titled versions of their basic presentations. Among the sources most likely to yield texts of speeches on the subject of Government and standards are the published proceedings of both the American Standards Association and the Standard Engineers Society.

Government agencies engaged in the promulgation and utilization of standards and specifications are guided by regulations which cover in detail all aspects of organization and procedure. Typical of published regulations of this type is STANDARDIZATION POLICIES, PROCEDURES AND INSTRUCTIONS, Defense Standardization Manual M200A, issued by the Defense Supply Agency and available from the Government Printing Office on a subscription basis. The basic compilation was published in 1962 and supplementary pages have been periodically issued since that date.

The Navy Standardization Board, in August 1963, issued a revised edition of NAVY GUIDE FOR SPECIFICATIONS, STANDARDS AND QUALIFIED PRODUCT LISTS. This 67-page document is for internal use only.

The General Services Administration is guided by the contents of Chapter VI of GSA Regulations, Title 1, COMMODITY STANDARDIZATION. Part 1 of this chapter "prescribes policies and methods for commodity standardization activities of Federal agencies in support of their supply management operations." Part 2 provides for the development and use of specifications and standards by all Federal agencies. Subsequent parts and appendices discuss the Federal Catalog System, Inspection and Testing, and other requirements.

Many agencies of the Federal government issue standards and specifications documents. The previously-described MONTHLY CATALOG, U.S. GOVERNMENT PUBLICATIONS: the U.S. GOVERNMENT RESEARCH TECHNICAL REPORTS, and NUCLEAR SCIENCE ABSTRACTS list many of the published documents. Publications lists and catalogs prepared and distributed by individual departments and bureaus of the Government are also useful for locating standards publications. The following listings represent a sampling of publications available from various Federal agencies. They are designed to reflect the variety and scope of Government participation and to be illustrative and selective, rather than comprehensive.

National Bureau of Standards

The major publications series of the Bureau are designated as Handbooks, Miscellaneous Publications, Monographs, Applied Mathematics and Technical Notes. The Research Papers series consists of reprints of individual articles which have appeared in the NBS Journal of Research which is issued monthly in four parts: Section A--Physics and Chemistry; Section B--Mathematics and Mathematical Physics; Section C--Engineering and Instrumentation; Section D--Radio Science. Commercial Standards and Simplified Practice Recommendations, mentioned earlier, are issued by the Commodity Standards Division of the National Bureau of Standards. Examples of publications occurring within the various series are as follows:

Handbooks are recommended codes of engineering and industrial practice, including safety codes, developed in cooperation with the national organizations of the industry and others concerned.

Handbook 28. SCREW THREAD STANDARDS FOR FEDERAL SERVICES.
Issued in three parts between 1957 and 1960, with a 1963 supplement dated October 7, 1960.

Handbook 44. SPECIFICATIONS, TOLERANCES, AND REGULA-

TIONS FOR COMMERCIAL WEIGHING AND MEASURING DEVICES. 1962. 173 p.

Handbook 71. SPECIFICATION FOR DRY CELLS AND BATTERIES. 1959. 20 p.

Handbook 74. BUILDING CODE REQUIREMENTS FOR REINFORCED CONCRETE. 1960. 13 p.

Handbook 82. WEIGHTS AND MEASURES ADMINISTRATION. 1962. 190 p.

Handbook 93. SAFETY STANDARD FOR NON-MEDICAL X-RAY AND SEALED GAMMA-RAY SOURCES. Part I. General. January 3, 1964.

Handbook 95. UNITED STATES STANDARD FOR THE COLORS OF SIGNAL LIGHTS. August 21, 1964. 30 p.

A book bargain as well as a convenience for reference is Handbook 77, issued in 1961. Its three volumes are collectively entitled PRECISION MEASUREMENT AND CALIBRATION. Volume I covers electricity and electronics; Volume II, heat and mechanics; and Volume III, optics, metrology and radiation. The 2,841 pages include previously published Circulars, Research Papers, and technical journal articles authored by members of the NBS staff. The documents span a period of more than forty years and represent a small fraction of the Bureau's publications. Many of the reprinted documents include lengthy bibliographies which list additional relevant NBS reports.

Falling within the Miscellaneous Publications series are the annual reports of the Bureau, the most recently published of which is 1963 RESEARCH HIGHLIGHTS OF THE NATIONAL BUREAU OF STANDARDS. 246 p. It covers the fiscal year 1963 and reviews the Bureau's efforts and accomplishments, especially in the areas of basic measurement standards, standard reference data, engineering measurement standards, standard reference materials, radio propagation, data-processing systems, and building research. Appendices give information on the organization of the NBS, a summary of NBS staff, personnel of advisory committees and a list of the Bureau's publications and patents during the fiscal year.

Annual reports of the NBS-sponsored National Conferences on WEIGHTS AND MEASURES, and the PROCEEDINGS OF THE STANDARDS LABORATORY CONFERENCES are also Miscellaneous Publications of the Bureau. Additional examples:

M230. STANDARDIZATION ACTIVITIES IN THE UNITED STATES; A DESCRIPTIVE DIRECTORY. 1960. 210 p.

M243. INDEX TO THE REPORTS OF THE NATIONAL CONFERENCE ON WEIGHTS AND MEASURES; FROM THE FIRST TO THE FORTY-FIFTH, 1905 to 1960. 1962. 74 p.

M247. WEIGHTS AND MEASURES STANDARDS OF THE UNITED STATES, A BRIEF HISTORY. 1963. 103 p.

M250. CALIBRATION AND TEST SERVICES OF THE NATIONAL BUREAU OF STANDARDS. 1963. 103 p.

M241. STANDARD MATERIALS ISSUED BY THE NATIONAL BUREAU OF STANDARDS; A DESCRIPTIVE LIST WITH PRICES. 1962. 32 p.

M260-1 PREPARATION OF NBS WHITE CAST IRON SPECTROCHEMICAL STANDARDS. 1964. 31 p.

Formerly in the discontinued Circulars series, but now included among Miscellaneous Publications series are the lists of publications of the Bureau. The following should be consulted for a 63-year view of NBS publications:

Circular 460. PUBLICATIONS OF THE NATIONAL BUREAU OF STANDARDS 1901 to June 30, 1947. 375 p.

SUPPLEMENT TO NBS CIRCULAR 460, SUPPLEMENTARY PUBLICATIONS OF THE NATIONAL BUREAU OF STANDARDS JULY 1, 1947 to June 30, 1957. 373 p.

Miscellaneous Publication 240. PUBLICATIONS OF THE NATIONAL BUREAU OF STANDARDS JULY 1, 1957 to June 30, 1960. 391 p.

SUPPLEMENTARY LIST OF PUBLICATIONS OF THE NATIONAL BUREAU OF STANDARDS JULY 1, 1960 to December 31, 1963.

37 p.

If publication volume is any measure of the Bureau's service then compare the number of pages in Circular 460 which spans a 46-year period with those in MP240 which spans a 4-year period.

Both the National Bureau of Standards' Technical News Bulletin and its Journal of Research keep readers up-to-date on publications of the Bureau itself and of the Bureau's staff in outside journals.

Monographs are usually contributions to the technical literature which are too lengthy for publication in the Journal of Research:

Monograph 15. CALIBRATION OF LINE STANDARDS OF LENGTH AND MEASURING TAPES AT THE NATIONAL BUREAU OF STANDARDS. 1960. 11p. Monograph 62. TESTING OF METAL VOLUMETRIC STANDARDS. 1963. 12 p.

Technical Notes series provides a means for making available scientific data of transient or limited interest. Technical Note 194, issued June 1963 is entitled NATIONAL STANDARD REFERENCE DATA PROGRAM: BACKGROUND INFORMATION (18 p.). It is the description of a program which will make available standard reference data, i.e., critically evaluated data on the physical and chemical properties of materials, authoritatively documented as to reliability, accuracy, and source.

A series that appears to have limited distribution for economy reasons are releases called SUMMARY TECHNICAL REPORTS which summarize individual instances of NBS activities. Some recent ones include:

STR-2787. MEASUREMENT OF STANDARD CELLS. December 1963. 15 p.

STR-2922. PRECISION OF THE U.S. FREQUENCY STANDARD. January 1964. 3 p.

STR-2909. GRAPHITE PARTICLES IN CAST IRON: PROPOSED STANDARDS FOR THEIR CLASSIFICATION EVALUATED. October 1963. 4 p.

STR-2973. NBS ADOPTS INTERNATIONAL SYSTEM OF UNITS.

February 1964. 5 p.

STR-2942. ACCURACY OF SPECTRAL TRANSMITTANCE STANDARDS INVESTIGATED. February 1964. 4 p.

STR-3072. TEN YEARS OF PROGRESS IN RADIO STANDARDS. September 1964. 16 p.

These releases are collectively known as TECHNICAL NEWS FROM U.S. DEPARTMENT OF COMMERCE, NATIONAL BUREAU OF STANDARDS. They are not indexed in the Bureau's LIST OF PUBLICATIONS.

A recent review of the work of the National Bureau of Standards in basic and engineering measurement standards for science and technology was prepared as a staff report in the reference below:

THE NBS AND MEASUREMENT STANDARDS. Electro-Technology 74:91-99, October 1964.

Public Health Service

U.S. Public Health Service. PUBLIC HEALTH SERVICE DRINKING WATER STANDARDS. Publication No. 956. Washington, D.C.: U.S. Public Health Service, 1962. 61 p.

Effective April 5, 1962 as the standards to which drinking water and water supply systems used by carriers and others subject to Federal quarantine regulations must conform. Endorsed by the American Water Works Association as minimum standards for all water supplies.

U.S. Public Health Service. REPORT OF PUBLIC HEALTH SERVICE TECHNICAL COMMITTEE ON PLUMBING STANDARDS. Publication No. 1038. Washington, D.C.: U.S. Department of Health, Education, and Welfare, 1962. 147 p.

A proposed revision of the National Plumbing Code, American Standards Association, ASA - A40.8-1955.

U.S. Public Health Service. A SANITARY STANDARD FOR MANUFACTURED ICE; RECOMMENDATIONS OF THE PUBLIC HEALTH SERVICE RELATING TO MANUFACTURE, PROCESSING, STORAGE AND TRANSPORTATION. Publication No. 1183. Washington, D.C.: Government Printing Office, 1964. 7 p.

U.S. Public Health Service. MILK ORDINANCE AND CODE. Publication No. 229. Washington, D.C.: Government Printing Office, 1953. 242 p.

United States Congress

The standardization activities of Federal Government agencies are authorized by laws which explicitly or implicitly define such activity. During the past several years the U.S. Congress has enacted several laws, and is considering others, which have established standards in such areas as radiation protection, automobile safety, and weights and measures. Published hearings provide general background information as well as pro and con testimony on the proposed legislation.

U.S. Congress. Joint Committee on Atomic Energy. RADIATION STANDARDS, INCLUDING FALLOUT; HEARINGS BEFORE THE SUBCOMMITTEE ON RESEARCH, DEVELOPMENT, AND RADIATION, EIGHTY-SEVENTH CONGRESS, SECOND SESSION. Parts I & II. 1040 p. SUMMARY ANALYSIS OF HEARINGS. 62 p. Washington, D.C.: Government Printing Office, 1962.

U.S. Congress. Joint Committee on Atomic Energy. FALLOUT, RADIATION STANDARDS, AND COUNTERMEASURES; HEARINGS BEFORE THE SUBCOMMITTEE ON RESEARCH, DEVELOPMENT, AND RADIATION, EIGHTY-EIGHTH CONGRESS, FIRST SESSION. Part I & II. Washington, D.C.: Government Printing Office, 1963. 1296 p.

U.S. Congress. Joint Committee on Atomic Energy. RADIATION PROTECTION CRITERIA AND STANDARDS: THEIR BASIS AND USE; HEARINGS BEFORE THE SUBCOMMITTEE ON RADIATION, EIGHTY-SIXTH CONGRESS, SECOND SESSION. Washington, D.C.: Government Printing Office, 1960. 820 p.

A 71-page SUMMARY-ANALYSIS of these hearings was issued October 1960, and a 97-page INDEX TO HEARINGS in June of 1961.

U.S. Congress. Joint Committee on Atomic Energy. SELECTED MATERIALS ON RADIATION PROTECTION CRITERIA STANDARDS: THEIR

BASIS AND USE. EIGHTY-SIXTH CONGRESS, SECOND SESSION. Washington, D.C.: Government Printing Office, 1960. 1244 p.

A compilation of statements by industry spokesmen, scientists, and labor and government representatives in preparation for the 1960 hearings listed above, RADIATION PROTECTION CRITERIA AND STANDARDS: THEIR BASIS AND USE. Included is a list of groups interested in radiation protection standards, and a summary of basic concepts underlying such standards. Several of the papers in the first chapter present a substantial amount of discussion of standardization in general, the history of standardization, the development of health and safety standards, and the organizations interested in them.

U. S. Congress. House. Committee on Science and Astronautics. AMENDING THE STANDARD CONTAINER ACT OF 1928; HEARINGS, EIGHTY-EIGHTH CONGRESS, FIRST SESSION ON H.R. 5792 SUPERSEDED BY H.R. 9334. Washington, D.C.: Government Printing Office, 1963. 36 p. REPORT TO ACCOMPANY H.R. 9334. 8 p.

U.S. Congress. House. Committee on Science and Astronautics. METRIC SYSTEM; HEARINGS BEFORE SUBCOMMITTEE NO. 1, EIGHTY-SEVENTH CONGRESS, FIRST SESSION, ON H.R. 269 and H.R. 2049. Washington, D.C.: Government Printing Office, 1961. 74 p.

U.S. Congress. House. Committee on Science and Astronautics. PROVIDING FOR A SURVEY TO DETERMINE PRACTICABILITY OF ADOPTING METRIC SYSTEM OF WEIGHTS AND MEASURES; REPORT FROM COMMITTEE ON SCIENCE AND ASTRONAUTICS TO ACCOMPANY H.R. 2049. Washington, D.C.: Government Printing Office, 1961. 6 p.

U.S. Congress. House. Committee on Interstate and Foreign Commerce. NATIONAL MILK SANITATION ACT OF 1957; HEARINGS BEFORE A SUBCOMMITTEE OF THE COMMITTEE ON INTERSTATE AND FOREIGN COMMERCE; EIGHTY-FIFTH CONGRESS, SECOND SESSION ON H.R. 7794 and H.R. 9286. Washington, D.C.: Government Printing Office,

1958. 176 p.
The bills' purpose was to protect the public health and to promote the public interest and to establish standards of identity, sanitation standards, and sanitation practices for the production, processing, transportation, sale, and offering for sale of fluid milk and fluid milk products shipped in interstate commerce. Hearings on similar bills were held during the 86th Congress, 2nd Session, April 26, 27, 28, 1960 and during the 87th Congress, 1st Session, July 31, August 1st, and August 30th, 1961.

U.S. Congress. House. Committee on Interstate and Foreign Commerce. AUTOMOBILE SEAT BELT STANDARDS; HEARINGS BEFORE THE SUBCOMMITTEE ON HEALTH AND SAFETY, EIGHTY-SEVENTH CONGRESS, SECOND SESSION ON H.R. 134. Washington, D.C.: Government Printing Office, 1962. 46 p.
Seven and nine-page reports to accompany H.R. 134 were issued June 11, 1963 and November 26, 1963, respectively.

U.S. Congress. House. Committee on Interstate and Foreign Commerce. MOTOR VEHICLE SAFETY; HEARING BEFORE THE SURFACE TRANSPORTATION SUB-COMMITTEE, EIGHTY-SIXTH CONGRESS, SECOND SESSION ON H.R. 1341. Washington, D.C.: Government Printing Office, 1960. 22 p.

U.S. Congress. House. Committee on Interstate and Foreign Commerce. MOTOR VEHICLE SAFETY STANDARDS; HEARINGS BEFORE SUBCOMMITTEE, EIGHTY-SEVENTH CONGRESS, FIRST SESSION. Washington, D.C.: Government Printing Office, 1961. 381 p.

U.S. Congress. House. SAFETY STANDARDS FOR GOVERNMENT PASSENGER-CARRYING MOTOR VEHICLES. Report No. 715, EIGHTY-SIXTH CONGRESS, FIRST SESSION. Washington, D.C.: Government Printing Office, 1959. 11 p.

U.S. Congress. Senate. Committee on Commerce. UNIFORM TIME LEGISLATION; HEARINGS BEFORE THE COMMITTEE ON COMMERCE, EIGHTY-EIGHTH CONGRESS, FIRST SESSION ON S.1033, S.1195 and S.1394, BILLS RELATING TO A UNIFORM

SYSTEM OF TIME STANDARDS. Washington, D.C.: Government Printing Office, 1963. 107 p.

U.S. Congress. House. Committee on Interstate and Foreign Commerce. UNIFORM TIME; HEARING BEFORE A SUBCOMMITTEE ON COMMERCE AND FINANCE, EIGHTY-EIGHTH CONGRESS, SECOND SESSION, Washington, D.C.: Government Printing Office, 1964.

Consideration of various bills which would, in general, provide for the establishment of a more uniform national system of time standards and provide means of enforcing the national standards.

U.S. Congress. House. CONSUMER PROTECTION ACTIVITIES OF FEDERAL DEPARTMENTS AND AGENCIES; EIGHTH REPORT BY THE COMMITTEE ON GOVERNMENT OPERATIONS, EIGHTY-SEVENTH CONGRESS, FIRST SESSION. House Report No. 1241. Washington, D.C.: Government Printing Office, 1961. 338 p.

Tables on pp. 50-51 briefly describe the classification and standardization activities of the various departments and agencies. Fuller description is supplied in the text. For example, it is noted that the Federal Aviation Agency is responsible for medical standards for civilian aviation personnel; that the Department of Agriculture is responsible for the standardization, grading and inspection of grain, naval stores, agricultural commodities; for graded meat inspection; for standardization of certain containers; for cotton classification and tobacco grading; and for quality standards for seeds.

U.S. Congress. Joint Committee on Printing. GOVERNMENT PAPER SPECIFICATIONS STANDARDS. Washington, D.C.: Government Printing Office, 1959 to date.

A subscription service with supplementary material, Part 1 contains detailed standard specifications; Part 2 gives testing standards; Part 3 consists of definitive color standards; Part 4 contains Government Printing Office standards on packaging and packing.

U.S. Congress. Temporary National Economic Committee. INVESTIGATION OF CONCENTRATION OF ECONOMIC POWER; HEARINGS BEFORE THE TEMPORARY NATIONAL ECONOMIC COMMITTEE, SEVENTY-SIXTH CONGRESS, FIRST SESSION. Part 8. PROBLEMS OF THE CONSUMER. Washington, D.C. Government

Printing Office, 1939. pp. 3283-3491.

These old hearings are included because of the current re-focusing of attention on standards for consumer goods. Much of the testimony on problems facing the problems of consumers revolved around the need for standards since neither brand name, nor price was deemed to be a guide to quality.

Department of Agriculture

Various acts of Congress have made standards for specific agricultural products mandatory under certain conditions. Products falling under the requirements of these laws include rosin and turpentine, tobacco, grain, cotton, apples, pears, and grapes for export, and containers. In addition, voluntary standards for grades of fresh and processed fruits and vegetables, eggs, meat and poultry, dairy products and other agricultural products have been promulgated by the U.S. Department of Agriculture. A complete list of all these standards will be found in:

U.S. Department of Agriculture. Agricultural Marketing Service. A CHECKLIST OF U.S. STANDARDS FOR FARM PRODUCTS. AMS-210. Washington, D.C.: U.S. Department of Agriculture, 1964. 16 p.

This checklist also includes a list of publications of the U.S.D.A. dealing with some aspect or other of standardization. Several of these are:

Agricultural Handbook 157. GRADE NAMES USED IN U.S. STANDARDS FOR FARM PRODUCTS.

Miscellaneous Publication 604. STANDARDIZATION AND INSPECTION OF FRESH FRUITS AND VEGETABLES.

Home and Garden Bulletin 59. SHOPPERS' GUIDE TO U.S. GRADES FOR FOOD.

Agriculture Handbook 25. RECOMMENDED SPECIFICATIONS FOR STANDARD PACKS, CONTAINERS AND PACKAGING MATERIALS FOR POULTRY AND POULTRY PRODUCTS.

Agriculture Handbook 145. U.S. STANDARDS FOR SHELL EGG PACKS.

Marketing Bulletin 15. U.S. GRADES FOR BEEF.

Agriculture Handbook 51. FEDERAL AND STATE STAND-

ARDS FOR THE COMPOSITION OF MILK PRODUCTS.

AMS-177. OFFICIAL GRAIN STANDARDS OF THE UNITED STATES.

AMS-513. HISTORICAL REVIEW OF CHANGES IN THE GRAIN STANDARDS OF THE UNITED STATES.

AMS-520. OFFICIAL GRADE STANDARDS AND INSPECTION FOR FRESH FRUITS AND VEGETABLES.

U.S. Department of Agriculture. MARKETING: YEARBOOK OF AGRICULTURE, 1954. Washington, D.C.: Government Printing Office, 1954. 506 p.

"Grades, Standards, pp. 142-169 is a discussion of units and standards of measurement, price as a symbol of a standard, grades and grading, and compulsory grade labeling."

Federal Radiation Council

U.S. Federal Radiation Council. BACKGROUND MATERIAL FOR THE DEVELOPMENT OF RADIATION PROTECTION STANDARDS. Washington, D.C.: Government Printing Office, 1960-1961.

Report No. 1, dated May 13, 1960 (39 p.) provides a general philosophy of radiation protection for Federal agencies. Report No.2, dated September 1961 (19 p.) takes up the problem of providing guidance for Federal agencies in activities designed to limit the exposure of members of population groups to radiation from radioactive materials deposited in the body as a result of their occurrence in the environment. The most recent report, No. 5, was issued July 1964.

Federal Housing Administration

The Federal Housing Administration issues and revises periodically a series of publications on housing standards. They include the following:

U.S. Federal Housing Administration. MINIMUM PROPERTY STANDARDS FOR MULTIFAMILY HOUSING. Washington, D.C.: Government Printing Office, 1963. 511 p.

U.S. Federal Housing Administration. MINIMUM PROPERTY STANDARDS FOR URBAN RENEWAL REHABILITATION. Washington, D.C.: Government Printing Office, 1964. 56 p.

U.S. Federal Housing Administration. MINIMUM PROPERTY

STANDARDS FOR 1 and 2 LIVING UNITS. GENERAL REVISION NO. 4. Washington, D.C.: Government Printing Office, 1963. 78 p.

U.S. Federal Housing Administration. MINIMUM PROPERTY STANDARDS FOR MOBILE HOME COURTS. Washington, D.C.: Government Printing Office, 1962. 80 p.

U.S. Federal Housing Administration. MINIMUM DESIGN STANDARDS FOR COMMUNITY SEWERAGE SYSTEMS. Washington, D.C.: Government Printing Office, 1963. 65 p.

U.S. Federal Housing Administration. MINIMUM PROPERTY STANDARDS FOR SWIMMING POOLS. Washington, D.C.: Government Printing Office, 1962. 14 p.

Bureau of Public Roads

U.S. Bureau of Public Roads. STANDARD SPECIFICATIONS FOR CONSTRUCTION OF ROADS AND BRIDGES ON FEDERAL HIGHWAY PROJECTS. Washington, D.C.: Government Printing Office, 1961. 383 p.

U.S. Bureau of Public Roads. STANDARD PLANS FOR HIGHWAY BRIDGES. Washington, D.C.: Government Printing Office, 1962.

In four volumes covering concrete superstructures, structural steel superstructures, timber bridges, and typical continuous bridges. A list of references is part of each volume.

U.S. Bureau of Public Roads. MANUAL ON UNIFORM TRAFFIC CONTROL DEVICES FOR STREETS AND HIGHWAYS. Washington, D.C.: Government Printing Office, 1961. 33 p.

Department of Defense

U.S. Department of Defense. STANDARDIZATION POLICIES, PROCEDURES AND INSTRUCTIONS. Manual 200A. Washington, D.C.: Government Printing Office, 1962 to date. Various paging; looseleaf.

U.S. Department of Defense. DEPARTMENT OF DEFENSE DIRECTORY AND PLANNING SCHEDULE OF FSC CLASS AND AREA

ASSIGNMENTS. Standardization Directory SD 1. Washington, D.C.: Government Printing Office, 1962.

This publication lists the standardization responsibility assignment of each of the units within the Department of Defense. Listing is by Federal Supply Classification number. A total of 575 FSC classes and standardization areas are included. Issued quarterly.

U.S. Department of Defense. DEPARTMENT OF DEFENSE MILITARY STANDARD REQUISITIONING AND ISSUE PROCEDURES. Alexandria, Virginia: Defense Supply Agency, 1964. 436 p.

U.S. Department of Defense. DIRECTORY OF POINTS OF CONTACT AND MAILING ADDRESSES. Washington, D.C.: Government Printing Office, 1963. 44 p.

A directory of mailing addresses to which drafts of Military and Federal Specifications, Standards, Standardization Plans, and other standardization documents are to be sent. Section I, Department of Army Addresses; Section II, Department of Navy Addresses; Section III, Department of Air Force Addresses; Section IV, Defense Supply Agency Addresses; Section V, Miscellaneous Department of Defense Addresses; Section Section VI, Non-Military Organizations Addresses.

Picatinny Arsenal. Plastics Technical Evaluation Center. DIRECTORY IN PLASTIC - KNOWLEDGEABLE GOVERNMENT PERSONNEL. AD 419 399. Washington, D.C.: U.S. Office of Technical Services, 1963. 248 p.

Includes names and affiliations of personnel dealing with specifications and standards on plastics, plastic materials and their applications.

National Academy of Sciences—National Research Council

National Academy of Sciences-National Research Council. SPECIFICATIONS AND CRITERIA FOR BIOCHEMICAL COMPOUNDS. Publication 719. Washington, D.C.: National Academy of Sciences-National Research Council, 1960. 122 sheets.

A 251-page Supplement One was published in 1963.

National Academy of Sciences-National Research Council. STATUS REPORT ON STANDARDIZATION OF RADIONUCLIDES IN THE UNITED STATES. Publication 270. Washington, D.C.:

National Academy of Sciences-National Research Council, 1953. 20 p.

National Academy of Sciences-National Research Council. Materials Advisory Board. RECOMMENDED QUALITY STANDARDS FOR TUNGSTEN SHEET PRODUCED IN THE REFRACTORY METAL SHEET ROLLING PROGAM. AD 437 606. Washington, D.C.: U.S. Office of Technical Services, 1964. 26 p.

National Academy of Sciences-National Research Council. RECOMMENDED MINIMUM STANDARDS FOR SHIPMENT OF LABORATORY PRIMATES. Publication 971. National Academy of Sciences-National Research Council, 1962. 24 p.

National Academy of Sciences-National Research Council. MEASUREMENTS AND STANDARDS OF RADIOACTIVITY. Publication 573. Washington, D.C.: National Academy of Sciences-National Research Council, 1958. 155 p.

Proceedings of a three-day conference organized by the NAS-NRC Subcommittee on Standards and Measurements of Radioactivity.

National Academy of Sciences-National Research Council. Food and Nutrition Board. RECOMMENDED DIETARY ALLOWANCES. Publication 1146. Washington, D.C.: National Academy of Sciences-National Research Council, 1964. 59 p.

Sixth revision of a publication first issued in 1943 whose "final objective ... is to permit and to encourage the development of food practices by the population of the United States that will allow for greatest dividends in health and in disease prevention. An appendix contains the dietary allowances and standards for adults developed by other countries, by the FAO, and jointly by FAO/WHO.

National Academy of Sciences-National Research Council. FOOD CHEMICAL CODEX, PART I. Publication 1143. Washington, D.C.: National Academy of Sciences-National Research Council, 1963.

The first published, organized, national standards for food-additive chemicals. Consists of a series of Monographs issued in looseleaf form on a subscription basis. The Codex will be published in book form in 1966.

Atomic Energy Commission

U.S. Atomic Energy Commission. MANUAL OF STANDARD PROCEDURES NYO-7400 (Revised). Washington, D.C.: U.S. Office of Technical Services, 1962. 416 p.
A manual of chemical procedures.

U.S. Atomic Energy Commission. CONFERENCE ON CLEAN ROOM SPECIFICATIONS; SANDIA CORPORATION FOR THE U.S. ATOMIC ENERGY COMMISSION. SCR-652. Washington, D.C.: Office of Technical Services, 1963. 121 p.

U.S. Atomic Energy Commission. SUMMARY REPORT ON AN AEC SYMPOSIUM ON PACKAGING AND REGULATORY STANDARDS FOR SHIPPING RADIOACTIVE MATERIAL. TID-7651. Washington, D.C.: U.S. Office of Technical Services, 1962. 417 p.

Federal Aviation Agency

U.S. Federal Aviation Agency. AIRCRAFT ENGINE AND PROPELLER SPECIFICATIONS AND TYPE CERTIFICATE DATA SHEETS. Washington, D.C.: Government Printing Office, 1963. 635 p.
Reprint of part of a current subscription service which also exists for AIRCRAFT SPECIFICATIONS.

U.S. Federal Aviation Agency. STANDARD SPECIFICATIONS FOR THE CONSTRUCTION OF AIRPORTS. Washington, D.C.: Government Printing Office, 1959. 588 p.
18-page Supplement 1 was published in 1961.

Office of the Federal Register

U.S. Office of the Federal Register. CODE OF FEDERAL REGULATIONS. Washington, D.C.: Government Printing Office. Various dates and paginations.
The Code of Federal Regulations contains the regulations issued by the various agencies of the Federal Government which have been granted the authority to do so by Congressional statutes. The Çodes consist of 50 books referred to as Titles. Title 21-Food and Drugs, Chapter I, Food and Drug Administration contains the standards of identity for foods and food products issued by the FDA. The individual books are issued as Special

Editions of the Federal Register in which the regulations are originally published.

Food and Drug Administration

The Food and Drug Administationa distributes unofficial prints of definitions and standards of identity for food and food products. These definitions and standards are initially published in the Federal Register, cumulated and reprinted annually with revisions as a Special Edition of the Federal Register. See above under Office of the Federal Register.

The unofficial prints are reprints from the Federal Register each reprint assembling the definitions and standards dealing with groups of food products. Some examples follow:

U.S. Food and Drug Administration. CEREAL FLOURS AND RELATED PARTS: DEFINITIONS AND STANDARDS UNDER THE FEDERAL FOOD, DRUG AND COSMETIC ACT. F.D.C. REGS., PART 15. Washington, D.C.: U.S. Food and Drug Administration, 1961. 14 p. Part 14 is CHOCOLATE AND COCOA PRODUCTS; Part 17, BAKERY PRODUCTS; Part 20, FROZEN DESSERTS.

A complete list of these reprints may be found in Price List 11, HOME ECONOMICS, FOODS AND COOKING, available free from the Government Printing Office, Washington, D.C. The Gunderson and Ferguson book, FOOD STANDARDS AND DEFINITIONS IN THE UNITED STATES, noted in Section III, gives a good description of the food standard activities of various government agencies.

U.S. Food and Drug Administration. WHAT CONSUMERS SHOULD KNOW ABOUT FOOD STANDARDS. Washington, D.C.: U.S. Food and Drug Administration, 1963. 12 p.

Bureau of Mines

U.S. Bureau of Mines. PROPOSED STANDARDIZATION OF COAL MINE EXAMINATION RECORDS. Information Circular 8081. Washington, D.C.: U.S. Bureau of Mines, 1962. 16 p.

U.S. Bureau of Mines. FEDERAL COAL MINES SAFETY ACT AND FEDERAL MINE SAFETY CODES---INTERPRETATIONS AND APPLICATIONS. Information Circular 8149. Washington, D.C.:

U.S. Bureau of Mines, 1963. 26 p.

Bureau of Ships

U.S. Bureau of Ships. STANDARDIZATION MANUAL. NAVSHIPS 250-350. Washington, D.C.: U.S. Bureau of Ships, Navy Department, 1955 to date.

This publication consists of six parts called chapters:

Chapter 1. Basic Standardization Information.
Chapter 2. Preferred Numbers.
Chapter 3. Inch-Millimeter Conversions and Designating Significant Figures.
Chapter 4. Standardized Requirements for Bureau of Ships Technical Reports.
Chapter 5. Using Technical Societies for Standardization.
Chapter 6. Cross Index, Industry-Military Specifications & Standards.

The introduction to Chapter 1 of this STANDARDIZATION MANUAL states that it is intended as "a medium for making known throughout the Bureau such basic standardization information as may prove useful in the performance of the Bureau's mission."

Interstate Commerce Commission

U.S. Interstate Commerce Commission. MOTOR CARRIER SAFETY REGULATIONS. Washington, D.C.: Government Printing Office, 1961. 78 p.

This publication incorporates specifications for parts and accessories of motor vehicles, such as, saddle-mounts, towbars, fuel tanks, first-aid kits, electric lanterns, heaters, reflectors, and turn signal systems. The contents of this booklet are part of Title 49 - Transportation - of the CODE OF FEDERAL REGULATIONS. Amendments to or changes in existing specifications, as well as proposed specifications, appear in issues of the FEDERAL REGISTER.

Section 5

ASSOCIATIONS AND SOCIETIES

Section 5

ASSOCIATIONS AND SOCIETIES

Several of the directories described in Section 1 provide detailed information about the purposes and programs of most of the organizations which are listed in this section. The intention here is to provide a guide to the standards and specifications publications available from the many trade associations and technical societies that produce such documents. Whenever feasible the specific title of the publication is given. In cases where the standards output of the organization is too voluminous to list completely, a general description of its publications is given along with the title of the catalog or list of publications which it has available. Over 250 organizations are represented here. There are at least an additional one hundred more participating in the formulation of standards and specifications by sponsoring or co-sponsoring them through the procedures of the American Standards Association, the American Society for Testing and Materials, the Commodity Standards Division of the U.S. National Bureau of Standards, or an international body. Also, there exist associations of associations which cooperate in the formulating of industry-wide standards, as well as industry-sponsored ad hoc groups for this purpose.

In discussing the question of why so many standards organizations exist, one writer has made the following observation: "In posing this question one wonders what the term 'standards organizations' means? Do we mean organizations whose sole objective is the development of standards? If it is, we can safely conclude there are none in existence today in the United States, If by organizations we mean those which as part of their activities are engaged in the development of standards, then our answer is in the affirmative to the extent of several hundred such organizations. And, if we define organizations as those solely concerned with standardization work but which do not develop standards, then we find only the Standards Engineers Society and the American Standards Association providing such services."[1]

The information given for each association has been compiled, for the most part, from their own publications. When available notation has been made of current journal articles which further describe the work of the association.

Acoustical Materials Association, 335 East 45th Street, New York 17, New York.
INSTALLATION RECOMMENDATIONS.

Aerospace Industries Association of America, 1725 De Sales Street, N.W. Washington 6, D.C.
NATIONAL AEROSPACE STANDARDS-ALPHABETICAL INDEX. NATIONAL AEROSPACE STANDARDS-NUMERICAL INDEX. Lists approximately 1000 standards on machinery, assemblies, parts, and components, procedures and measurements. Witt, G.E. STANDARDIZATION...IN THE AEROSPACE INDUSTRIES. Standards Engineering 13-6-8, February-March 1961.

Agricultural Ammonia Institute, 703 Dupont Building, 22 South Second Street, Memphis 3, Tennessee
STANDARDS FOR THE STORAGE AND HANDLING OF ANHYDROUS AMMONIA.

Air-Conditioning and Refrigeration Institute, 1815 North Fort Meyer Drive, Arlington 8, Virginia.
ARI STANDARDS.
Several dozen standards on unitary air-conditioners; heat-transfer equipment; air-conditioning and refrigeration systems equipment; valves, driers, fittings, and accessories; self-contained ice-makers; cooling towers; water coolers; mobile air-conditioning and refrigeration.

Air Diffusion Council, 333 North Michigan Avenue, Chicago, Illinois.
STANDARD AD-63, MEASUREMENT OF ROOM-TO-ROOM SOUND TRANSMISSION THROUGH PLENUM AIR SYSTEMS. EQUIPMENT TEST CODE.

Air Filter Institute, Box 85, Station E, Louisville, Kentucky.

---

1. Ainsworth, Cyril. WHY SO MANY STANDARDS ORGANIZATIONS? STANDARDS ENGINEERING 13:14-16, December 1961.

AFI DUST SPOT TEST CODE, 1960.
AN ANALYSIS OF THE A.F.I. TEST CODE.
CODE FOR TESTING AIR CLEANING DEVICES USED IN GENERAL VENTILATION.

Air Moving and Conditioning Association, 205 W. Touhy Avenue, Park Ridge, Illinois.

PUBLICATION 99 - STANDARDS AND RECOMMENDED PRACTICES.
Contains all standards and recommended practices of the Association other than test codes.
PUBLICATION 20 - STANDARD TEST CODE FOR STEAM UNIT HEATERS.
PUBLICATION 210 - STANDARD TEST CODE FOR AMD'S.
PUBLICATION 300 - RECOMMENDED PRACTICE FOR SOUND TESTING OF AMD'S.

Alumina Ceramic Manufacturers Association, 53 Park Place, New York 7, New York.

STANDARDS OF THE ALUMINA CERAMIC MANUFACTURERS ASSOCIATION.
Cover properties, test methods, design fundamentals, dimensional tolerances, visual requirements, quality assurance standards, resistance to nuclear radiation, general manufacturing procedures, metallizing, and applications.
SPECIFICATION FOR IMPERVIOUS, HIGH STRENGTH ALUMINA CERAMICS FOR ELECTRICAL AND ELECTRONIC APPLICATIONS.
SPECIFICATION FOR IMPERVIOUS, HIGH STRENGTH ALUMINA CERAMICS FOR MECHANICAL APPLICATIONS.

Aluminum Association, 42 Lexington Avenue, New York 17, New York.

STANDARDS FOR WROUGHT ALUMINUM MILL PRODUCTS, 5th edition.
SPECIFICATION FOR STRUCTURES OF ALUMINUM ALLOYS.
DRAFTING STANDARDS - ALUMINUM EXTRUDED AND TUBULAR PRODUCTS, 4th edition, and SUPPLEMENT.
NOMENCLATURE FOR WROUGHT ALUMINUM MILL PRODUCTS; STANDARDS FOR PAINTED ALUMINUM SHEET; STANDARDS FOR ANODICALLY COATED ALUMINUM ALLOYS FOR ARCHITECTURAL APPLICATIONS; TENTATIVE PACKAGING STANDARDS FOR BARESTRANDED ALUMINUM CONDUCTOR AND ACSR; AMERICAN STANDARD ALLOY AND TEMPER DESIGNATIONS SYSTEMS FOR WROUGHT ALUMINUM; ULTRASONIC QUALITY LIMITS FOR ALUMINUM MILL PRODUCTS; PROTECTIVE OIL FOR ALUMINUM.

Aluminum Smelters Research Institute, 20 North Wacker Drive, Chicago 6, Illinois.

REVISED ALUMINUM SCRAP CLASSIFICATIONS.

American Association of Cereal Chemists, 1955 University Avenue, St. Paul 4, Minnesota.

CEREAL LABORATORY METHODS.

American Association of Nurserymen, 835 Southern Building, Washington 5, D.C.

AMERICAN STANDARD FOR NURSERY STOCK, ASA Z60. 1-1958.

THE STANDARD FOR HOME LANDSCAPING.

American Association of State Highway Officials, 917 National Press Building, Washington 4, D.C.

CODE HB-8 STANDARD SPECIFICATIONS FOR HIGHWAY BRIDGES.

CODE GP-1 SPECIFICATIONS FOR GENERAL PROVISIONS.

CODE CP-2 SPECIFICATIONS FOR CONCRETE PAVEMENT CONSTRUCTION.

CODE DS-2 A POLICY ON DESIGN STANDARDS--INTERSTATE SYSTEM.

CODE DSOF-1 GEOMETRIC DESIGN STANDARDS FOR HIGHWAYS OTHER THAN FREEWAYS.

CODE UT-2 MANUAL OF UNIFORM TRAFFIC CONTROL DEVICES FOR STREETS AND HIGHWAYS.

CODE HG-1 SPECIFICATIONS FOR HIGHWAY GUARDS.

CODE SS-1 SPECIFICATIONS FOR DESIGN AND CONSTRUCTION OF STRUCTURAL SUPPORTS FOR HIGHWAY SIGNS.

AASHO GOAL; UNIFORM SPECS. Engineering News 170:19-20 May 9, 1963.

American Association of Textile Chemists and Colorists, Lowell Technological Institute, Box 28, Lowell, Massachusetts.

TECHNICAL MANUAL OF THE AMERICAN ASSOCIATION OF TEXTILE CHEMISTS AND COLORISTS.

This annually revised manual contains over 100 AATCC standard test methods for end-use performance characteristics of textiles.

American Boat and Yacht Council, 420 Lexington Avenue, New York 17, New York.

Current list of accepted standards include:

A-2 SEA COCKS, THROUGH-HULL CONNECTIONS, SEA STRAINERS AND WATER SCOOPS; A-3 DESIGN, CONSTRUCTION AND INSTALLATION OF GALLEY

STOVES; A-4 FIRE-FIGHTING EQUIPMENT; A-6 INSTALLATION, USE AND MAINTENANCE OF REFRIGERATION AND AIR-CONDITIONING EQUIPMENT; A-8 SEWAGE TREATMENT DEVICES.
E-1 GROUNDING OF DIRECT-CURRENT SYSTEMS; E-3 WIRING IDENTIFICATION; E-4 LIGHTNING PROTECTION; E-6 INSTALLATION OF ALTERNATING-CURRENT RECTIFIERS.
H-2 ENGINE AND FUEL-TANK COMPARTMENT VENTILATION; H-3 DESIGN, LOCATION AND CONSTRUCTION OF HATCHES AND DOORS, COCKPITS AND SCUPPERS; H-6 LOCATION AND VISIBILITY OF NAVIGATION LIGHTS; H-7 METAL FASTENINGS IN WOODEN VESSELS; H-9 LIFE-SAVING EQUIPMENT AND ITS STOWAGE; H-12 AIDS TO SECURITY OF PERSONNEL ON DECK AND AIDS FOR REBOARDING FROM WATER.
P-1 INSTALLATION OF EXHAUST SYSTEMS; P-3 DETERMINING AND STATING THE HORSEPOWER RATING OF INBOARD GASOLINE ENGINES; P-4 DESIGN AND CONSTRUCTION OF INBOARD, LIQUID-COOLED GASOLINE ENGINES; P-10 INSTALLATION OF AIR-COOLED DIESEL AND GASOLINE ENGINES.

American Boiler Manufacturers Association, 1180 Raymond Boulevard, Newark 2, New Jersey.
1958 MANUAL--INDUSTRY STANDARDS AND ENGINEERING INFORMATION.
The standards cover boilers, superheaters, stokers, pulverized fuel equipment, air preheaters, and economizers.

American Bureau of Shipping, 45 Broad Street, New York 4, New York.
RULES FOR BUILDING AND CLASSING STEEL VESSELS.
RULES FOR BUILDING AND CLASSING STEEL VESSELS FOR SERVICE ON RIVERS AND INTERCOASTAL WATERWAYS.
REQUIREMENTS FOR THE CERTIFICATION OF THE CONSTRUCTION AND SURVEY OF CARGO GEAR ON MERCHANT VESSELS AND CODE OF RECOMMENDED PRECAUTIONS AGAINST ACCIDENTS CONNECTED WITH THE LOADING AND UNLOADING OF MERCHANT VESSELS.
GUIDE FOR THE CLASSIFICATION OF NUCLEAR SHIPS.

American Concrete Institute, 22400 West Seven Mile Road, Detroit 19, Michigan.
ACI BOOK OF STANDARDS, 1963.
Contains 17 current standards of the ACI except for Standard ACI 315-57, MANUAL OF STANDARD PRACTICE FOR DETAILING REINFORCED CONCRETE

STRUCTURES. All standards are available separately.

American Conference of Industrial Hygienists, 1014 Broadway, Cincinnati, Ohio 45202.

INDUSTRIAL VENTILATION--A MANUAL OF RECOMMENDED PRACTICE.
ANALYTICAL METHODS MANUAL.
GUIDE TO UNIFORM INDUSTRIAL HYGIENE CODES OR REGULATIONS.
STANDARD REPORTS OF OCCUPATIONAL HEALTH ACTIVITIES AMONG STATE AND LOCAL HEALTH AGENCIES.
THRESHOLD LIMIT VALUES.
DOCUMENTATION OF THRESHOLD LIMIT VALUES.

American Congress on Surveying and Mapping, 430 Woodward Building, 733 Fifteenth Street, N.W., Washington 5, D.C.

TECHNICAL STANDARDS FOR PROPERTY SURVEYS.
MINIMUM STANDARDS DETAIL REQUIREMENTS FOR LAND TITLE SURVEYS.

American Dental Association, 222 East Superior Street, Chicago 11, Illinois.

GUIDE TO DENTAL MATERIALS, 1963-1964.
Contains ADA Specifications for various dental alloys, cements, and other dental materials.

American Die Casting Institute, 366 Madison Avenue, New York 17, New York.

PRODUCT STANDARDS FOR DIE CASTINGS.
A compilation of seven engineering, eleven metallurgical, and nine Commercial Standards.

American Dry Milk Institute, 221 North LaSalle Street, Chicago 1, Illinois.

BULLETIN NO. 915 - RECOMMENDED SANITARY/ QUALITY CODE FOR THE DRY MILK INDUSTRY.
BULLETIN NO. 916 - STANDARDS FOR GRADES FOR THE DRY MILK INDUSTRY, INCLUDING METHODS OF ANALYSIS.

American Gas Association, Inc. Laboratories, 1032 West 62nd Street, Cleveland 3, Ohio.

LIST OF AMERICAN STANDARD APPROVAL REQUIREMENTS FOR GAS APPLIANCES.
This list contains some 50 approval, listing and installation standards in effect as of January 1, 1963. Air conditioning, central heating gas appliances, clothes dryers, counter appliances, deep fat fryers,

duct furnaces, hot plates, incinerators, portable ovens, ranges, refrigerators, room heaters, unit heaters, and water heaters are included.

American Gear Manufacturers Association. One Thomas Circle, Washington 5, D.C.

The PUBLICATIONS INDEX lists over 100 AGMA standards on Assembled-Enclosed Gearing, Assembled-Open Gearing, Unassembled Gears, Gear Systems, Tools, Cutters, Hobs, and a variety of components.
Jackson, J. Harper, Sr. GEAR MANUFACTURERS WORK FOR BETTER COMMUNICATIONS THROUGH STANDARDS. Magazine of Standards 33:304-305, October 1962.

American Home Economics Association, 1600 Twentieth Street, N.W., Washington 9, D.C.

ASA.Z61 - AMERICAN STANDARD DIMENSIONS, TOLERANCES AND TERMINOLOGY FOR HOME COOKING AND BAKING UTENSILS.

American Home Laundry Manufacturers' Association, 20 North Wacker Drive, Chicago 6, Illinois.

STANDARD SOIL REMOVAL TEST PROCEDURE MANUAL.
HOME LAUNDERING TERMS.

American Institute of Architects, 1735 New York Avenue, N.W., Washington 6, D.C.

SPECIFICATION WORK SHEETS for Excavating, Filling and Grading; Concrete Work; Masonry Work; Exterior Cut Stone; Precast Architectural Concrete; Structural Steel; Steel Joists; Steel Roof Decks; Precast Roof Decks; Pored Gypsum Roof Decks; Roofing and Sheet Metal; Hollow Metal Doors and Frames; Kalamein and Metal Covered Work; Rolling Metal Doors and Grilles; Steel Windows; Aluminum Windows; Lathing and Plastering; Ceramic and Quarry Tile; Terazzo.
ARCHITECTS HANDBOOK OF PROFESSIONAL PRACTICE. Chapter 14. Specifications.
AIA STANDARD FILING SYSTEM FOR PRODUCT LITERATURE.
AIA BUILDING PRODUCTS REGISTER.

American Institute of Chemical Engineers, 345 East 47th Street, New York 17, New York.

STANDARD TESTING PROCEDURES for Plate Distillation Columns; Evaporators; Solids Mixing Equipment; Mixing Equipment (Impeller Type); Centrifugal Pumps (Newtonian Liquids); Dryers (Rotary Continuous Direct-Heat Dryers);

Absorbers; Heat Exchangers (Shell and Tube Type Condensers); Heat Exchangers (Sensible Heat Transfer in Shell-and Tube-Type Equipment).

American Institute of Steel Construction, 101 Park Avenue, New York 17, New York.

S 302 - CODE OF STANDARD PRACTICE FOR BUILDINGS AND BRIDGES.
S305 - STANDARD SPECIFICATIONS AND LOAD TABLE, OPEN WEB STEEL JOISTS-LONGSPAN OR L SERIES.
S307 - SPECIFICATIONS FOR ARCHITECTURALLY EXPOSED STRUCTURAL STEEL.
S308 - DIMINSIONS, WEIGHTS AND PROPERTIES OF NEW LIGHT-WEIGHT FLANGE SHAPES.
S309 - DESIGN LOADS FOR HIGH STRENGTH BOLTS.
S310 - SPECIFICATION FOR THE DESIGN, FABRICATION AND ERECTION OF STRUCTURAL STEEL FOR BUILDINGS.
S311 - COMMENTARY ON THE AISC SPECIFICATION (S310).
S312 - ROLLED BEAM PROPERTIES FOR PLASTIC DESIGN.
S313 - STANDARD SPECIFICATIONS AND LOAD TABLE, OPEN WEB STEEL JOISTS - HIGH STRENGTH LONGSPAN OR LH SERIES.

American Institute of Timber Construction, 1757 K Street, N.W. Washington 6, D.C.

TIMBER CONSTRUCTION STANDARDS.
GUIDE SPECIFICATIONS FOR STRUCTURAL TIMBER FRAMING.
STANDARD FOR HEAVY TIMBER DECKING.
QUALITY STANDARDS FOR LAMINATED TIMBER CONSTRUCTION.

American Mining Congress, Ring Building, Washington 6, D.C.

M30.1-1957 AMERICAN STANDARD SPECIFICATIONS FOR ROOF BOLTING MATERIALS.
ASA M7.3-1958 CONSTRUCTION AND MAINTENANCE OF RAIL HAULAGE ROADS IN COAL MINES.
Includes Recommendations for Track Construction; Specification for Main Haulage Mine Ties; Accepted American Standards for Frogs, Switches and Turnouts, 60lb. Rail and Under; and Recommendations for Standard Turnouts.

American Nuclear Society, 244 East Ogden Avenue, Hinsdale, Illinois.

REPORT OF ACTIVITIES OF AMERICAN NUCLEAR SOCIETY STANDARDS COMMITTEE AS OF MAY 1963.

Includes Areas Under Investigation for Possible Standards Generation; Standards in Final Draft Stage and in Subcommittees; Other Standards Requiring Standards Committee Action; ANS-Generated Standards Ready for Standards Committee Action; ASA-N6 Standards Requiring Standards Committee Direction to ANS Representative for ASA Balloting; ANS-Generated Standards Submitted for ASA Processing; Other Standards of Interest to Committee Through ANS Representative. A subsequent report for the period October 1963 to May 1964 summarizes the activities of subcommittees and of ANS representatives to ASA sectional committees. A project of Subcommittee N6.9 of ASA Sectional Committee, N6, Reactor Safety Standards, is AN INDEX OF AMERICAN AND FOREIGN NUCLEAR SAFETY STANDARDS.

American Oil Chemists' Society, 35 E. Wacker Drive, Chicago 1, Illinois.

OFFICIAL AND TENTATIVE METHODS OF ANALYSIS.

American Petroleum Institute, 1271 Avenue of the Americas, New York 20, New York.

LIST OF PUBLICATIONS AND MATERIALS includes a list of more than 100 standards, specifications and recommended practices for or associated with belting; cable drilling tools; derricks and masts; tubular goods; valves, fittings, and flanges; rotary drilling equipment; hoisting tools; wire rope; oil well cements; production equipment; lease production vessels; drilling fluid materials; refining; safety and fire protection; and interdivisional standardization.

STANDARDIZATION OF OIL-FIELD EQUIPMENT, by C. C. Scharpenberg is Chapter 20 of the History of Petroleum Engineering, a 1961 publication of the American Petroleum Institute's Division of Production. This chapter discusses the history and scope of oil-field standardization and has an appendix listing 25 associations, societies and agencies which..."have rendered major services to the standardization of oil-field equipment."

American Public Health Association, 1790 Broadway, New York 19, New York.

STANDARD METHODS FOR THE EXAMINATION OF DAIRY PRODUCTS.

STANDARD METHODS FOR THE EXAMINATION OF WATER AND WASTEWATER.

RECOMMENDED METHODS FOR THE MICROBIOLOGICAL EXAMINATION OF FOODS.

RECOMMENDED PROCEDURES FOR THE BACTERIOLOGICAL EXAMINATION OF SEA WATER AND SHELLFISH.

SWIMMING POOLS AND OTHER PUBLIC BATHING PLACES.
Presents recommended practice for design, equipment and operation.

American Public Works Association, 1313 East 60th Street, Chicago 37, Illinois.
STANDARD SPECIFICATIONS FOR PUBLIC WORKS CONSTRUCTION.
This series includes the following titles: Soil Bituminous Stabilized Base Course for Roads and Streets; Bituminous Pavements; Sewers; Calcium Chloride Stabilization of Roads and Streets; Sidewalks and Curbs; Subgrades and Foundations for Pavements.
UNIFORM PUBLIC WORKS ENGINEERING CONSTRUCTION FORMS.
CONTRACTS AND SPECIFICATIONS FOR REMODELING BUILDINGS, article in 1959 YEARBOOK.
GUIDELINES FOR PREPARING EQUIPMENT SPECIFICATIONS, article in 1961 YEARBOOK.
PUBLIC WORKS STANDARDS FOR NEW SUBDIVISIONS, article in 1962 YEARBOOK.

American Railway Engineering Association, 59 East Van Buren Street, Chicago 5, Illinois.
MANUAL OF RECOMMENDED PRACTICE.
Includes Specifications and recommendations for roadway and ballast; track; buildings; wood bridges and trestles; masonry; highways; records and accounts; water; oil; and sanitation services; yards and terminals; iron and steel structures; wood preservation; waterways and harbors; maintenance of way work equipment; and waterproofing.

American Society for Testing and Materials, 1916 Race Street, Philadelphia, Pa.
1964 BOOK OF ASTM STANDARDS, 32 VOLUMES.
Supersedes the eleven-part 1961 Book of ASTM Standards and its supplements, and replaces most of the former compilations of standards on specific subjects. The 32 parts are to be revised annually, with publication dates scattered throughout the year. The size of each volume varies, the smallest having 352 pages, the largest 1090 pages. Number of standards per volume varies from 46 to 291, with a total of 3,542 in the 32 volumes. The parts are:
PART 1 STEEL PIPING MATERIALS.
PART 2 FERROUS CASTINGS.
PART 3 STEEL SHEET, STRIP, BAR, ROD, WIRE, CHAIN, AND SPRING; WROUGHT IRON BAR AND SHEET; METALLIC COATED PRODUCTS.
PART 4 STRUCTURAL STEEL; BOILER AND PRESSURE VESSEL

PLATE; STEEL RAILS, WHEELS, AND TIRES; BEARING STEEL; STEEL FORGINGS; FERRO-ALLOYS; FILLER METAL.
PART 5 COPPER AND COPPER ALLOYS (INCLUDING ELECTRICAL CONDUCTORS).
PART 6 LIGHT METALS AND ALLOYS (INCLUDING ELECTRICAL CONDUCTORS).
PART 7 NONFERROUS METALS AND ALLOYS (INCLUDING CORROSION TESTS); DIE-CAST METALS; ELECTRODEPOSITED METALLIC COATINGS; METAL POWDERS.
PART 8 MAGNETIC PROPERTIES; METALLIC MATERIALS FOR THERMOSTATS AND FOR ELECTRICAL RESISTANCE, HEATING, AND CONTACTS; MATERIALS FOR ELECTRON TUBES AND SEMI-CONDUCTOR DEVICES.
PART 9 CEMENT; LIME; GYPSUM.
PART 10 CONCRETE AND MINERAL AGGREGATES.
PART 11 BITUMINOUS MATERIALS FOR HIGHWAY CONSTRUCTION, WATERPROOFING, AND ROOFING; SOILS.
PART 12 MORTARS; CLAY AND CONCRETE PIPE AND TILE: MASONRY UNITS; ASBESTOS-CEMENT PRODUCTS; BUILDING STONE.
PART 13 REFRACTORIES; GLASS; CERAMIC MATERIALS.
PART 14 THERMAL INSULATION: ACOUSTICAL MATERIALS; JOINT SEALANTS; FIRE TESTS; BUILDING CONSTRUCTIONS.
PART 15 PAPER; PACKAGING; CELLULOSE; CASEIN; FLEXIBLE BARRIER MATERIALS.
PART 16 STRUCTURAL SANDWICH CONSTRUCTIONS; WOOD; ADHESIVES.
PART 17 PETROLEUM PRODUCTS-MOTOR FUELS; SOLVENTS; FUEL OILS; LUBRICATING OILS.
PART 18 PETROLEUM PRODUCTS-MEASUREMENT AND SAMPLING; LIQUIFIED PETROLEUM GASES; PURE LIGHT HYDROCARBONS; ENGINE TEST METHODS; LUBRICATING GREASE; PETROLEUM WAX.
PART 19 GASEOUS FUELS; COAL AND COKE.
PART 20 PAINT, VARNISH, LACQUER, AND RELATED PRODUCTS--MATERIALS SPECIFICATIONS AND TESTS; NAVAL STORES; INDUSTRIAL AROMATIC HYDROCARBONS.
PART 21 PAINT, VARNISH, LACQUER, AND RELATED PRODUCTS-TESTS FOR FORMULATED PRODUCTS AND APPLIED COATINGS.
PART 22 SORPTIVE MINERAL MATERIALS; SOAP; ENGINE ANTIFREEZES; WAX POLISHES; HALOGENATED ORGANIC SOLVENTS.
PART 23 INDUSTRIAL WATER; ATMOSPHERIC ANALYSIS.
PART 24 TEXTILE MATERIALS--METHODS AND DEFINITIONS, GENERAL.
PART 25 TEXTILE MATERIALS--FIBERS AND PRODUCTS; LEATHER.
PART 26 PLASTICS--SPECIFICATIONS (WITH CLOSELY RELATED TESTS).
PART 27 PLASTICS--GENERAL METHODS OF TESTING.
PART 28 RUBBER; CARBON BLACK; GASKETS.

PART 29 ELECTRICAL INSULATING MATERIALS.
PART 30 GENERAL TESTING METHODS; QUALITY CONTROL; APPEARANCE TESTS; TEMPERATURE MEASUREMENT; EFFECT OF TEMPERATURE.
PART 31 METALLOGRAPHY; NONDESTRUCTIVE TESTING; RADIOISOTOPES AND RADIATION EFFECTS; INDUSTRIAL CHEMICALS; EMISSION, ABSORPTION, AND MASS SPECTROSCOPY.
PART 32 CHEMICAL ANALYSIS OF METALS.
LIST OF PUBLICATIONS, MAY 1964. 74 p.
Annotated list of all the Society's publications with an index to major subjects.
INDEX TO STANDARDS, JULY 1964. 234 p.
Gives complete references to publications where standards or tentatives appear in their latest form. Annual.
YEAR BOOK. Annual.
Includes list of Technical Committees working on standards and names of members.
MATERIALS RESEARCH & STANDARDS.
Monthly journal with technical articles, news of association activities, up-to-date information on standards and other publications.
Harnden, G. H. THE ADMINISTRATIVE COMMITTEE ON STANDARDS; WHAT IT IS AND WHAT IT DOES. Materials Research & Standards 3:923-924, November 1963.
1964 BOOK OF ASTM STANDARDS TO BE PUBLISHED IN 32 PARTS. Materials Research & Standards 3:587-588, July 1963.
Clair, M. N. ASTM? Materials Research & Standards 2:661-663, August 1962.
ASTM ABROAD. Materials Research & Standards 1:886-889, November 1961.
INTERNATIONAL SYMPOSIUM ON PLASTICS TESTING AND STANDARDIZATION, 1959. 276 p.

American Society of Agricultural Engineers, Saint Joseph, Michigan.

AGRICULTURAL ENGINEER'S YEARBOOK.
Annual publication which includes ASAE standards, recommendations, and data relating to tractors, implements, structures, irrigation, drainage, livestock, crop drying and storage, bulk milk systems, and safety. Separate reprints of these standards are available.
The ASAE also publishes a monthly journal, AGRICULTURAL ENGINEERING, recent issues of which contained the following articles:
Kyle, J. T. FARM MACHINERY TESTING BY PUBLIC AGENCIES. Agricultural Engineering 44:432-3+ August 1963; Erratum 44:680, December 1963.
Tanquary, E.W. STANDARDIZATION--WORLD-WIDE. Agricultural Engineering 44:486-487, 496, September 1963.

Reviews various farm machinery standardizing organizations throughout the world; outlines procedures for establishing international technical standards.

American Society of Civil Engineers, 345 East 47th Street, New York 17, New York.

MANUAL AND REPORTS ON ENGINEERING PRACTICE. This reports series includes some standards, such as Manual 32, AMERICAN STANDARD BUILDING CODE REQUIREMENTS FOR EXCAVATIONS AND FOUNDATIONS.

American Society of Heating, Refrigerating and Air-Conditioning Engineers, 345 East 47th Street, New York 17, N.Y.

The following standards, and methods of rating and testing, and recommended practices are available from the ASHRAE:
12-58 REFRIGERATION TERMS AND DEFINITIONS; 13-53 HOME FREEZERS; HOUSEHOLD REFRIGERATORS; HOUSEHOLD ELECTRIC REFRIGERATORS; 14-59 CONDENSING UNITS, MECHANICAL; 15-58 SAFETY CODE FOR MECHANICAL REFRIGERATION; 16-61 ROOM AIR CONDITIONERS; 17-48 EXPANSION VALVES, REFRIGERANTS; 18-62 DRINKING WATER COOLERS WITH SELF-CONTAINED MECHANICAL REFRIGERATING SYSTEMS; 20-60 AIR-COOLED AND EVAPORATIVE CONDENSERS; 22-61 WATER-COOLED REFRIGERANT CONDENSERS; 23-59 COMPRESSORS, REFRIGERANT; 24-61 LIQUID COOLERS; 25-56 AIR COOLERS FOR REFRIGERATION; 26-56 MECHANICAL REFRIGERATION INSTALLATIONS ON SHIPBOARD; 28-57 CAPILLARY TUBES; 29-56 ICE MAKERS; 30-60 LIQUID CHILLING PACKAGES; 32-57 BOTTLED BEVERAGE COOLERS; 33-58 AIR-COOLING and AIR-HEATING COILS; 34-57 REFRIGERANTS; 35A-56 DRIERS, HIGH SIDE LIQUID-LINE; 36-62 MEASUREMENT OF SOUND POWER RADIATED FROM HEATING, REFRIGERATING AND AIR-CONDITIONING EQUIPMENT; 37-60 UNITARY AIR-CONDITIONING EQUIPMENT; 38-57 COOLING TOWERS, MECHANICAL DRAFT; 39-61 UNITARY HEAT PUMP EQUIPMENT; 40-61 HEAT OPERATED UNITARY AIR CONDITIONING EQUIPMENT FOR COOLING.

ASHRAE GUIDE AND DATA BOOK. FUNDAMENTALS AND EQUIPMENT, 1963.
As previously noted Chapter 67 of this manual contains an alphabetical listing by subjects of 200 standards and and codes issued by 60 organizations in the field.
Versagi, F. J. ASHRAE SPELLS OUT POLICY ON CODE, STANDARDS ACTIVITIES BY CHAPTERS. Air Conditioning, Heating & Refrigeration News 101:3, March 16, 1964.
Hutcheon, N. B. SOCIETY POLICY ON STANDARDS.

ASHRAE Journal 4:81,89, August 1962.
The 70th Annual Meeting of the ASHRAE, June 24-26, 1963 includes a Symposium on Federal Specifications.

American Society of Mechanical Engineers, 345 East 47th Street, New York 17, New York.

CATALOG OF ASME PUBLICATIONS.
Lists and describes guides and manuals developed by Committees of the Society and designated as ASME standards. Included are:
100 - PREFERRED STANDARDS FOR LARGE CONDENSING STEAM TURBINE-GENERATORS.
101 - OPERATION AND FLOW PROCESS CHARTS.
102 - SELF-APPRAISAL FORM FOR USE OF INDUSTRIAL PLANTS.
103 - PLANT LAYOUT TEMPLATES AND MODELS.
104 - ONE-PIECE METALLIC PISTON RINGS.
107 - PREFERRED STANDARDS FOR THE PRESENTATION OF FREQUENCY RESPONSE DATA.
108 - DESIGN OF TURBINE LUBRICATING SYSTEMS.
109 - HANDBOOK FOR SMALL SAWMILL OPERATORS.
110 - GLOSSARY OF TERMS IN NUCLEAR SCIENCE AND TECHNOLOGY.
111 - DESIGN OF MARINE PROPULSION LUBRICATING SYSTEMS.
112 - DIAPHRAGM ACTUATED CONTROL VALVE TERMINOLOGY.
ASME BOILER AND PRESSURE CODE.
POWER TEST CODES AND INSTRUMENTS AND APPARATUS.
The catalog includes a listing of American Standards on fasteners, flanges and flanged fittings, pipe, pipe fittings, and threads, screw threads, small tools and machine tool elements, gear design, dimensions and inspection, drafting techniques, safety, symbols and abbreviations. There is also a list of ASME standards under development.
MECHANICAL ENGINEERING, the Society's journal keeps up-to-date on ASME BOILER AND PRESSURE CODE changes.

American Specification Institute, 134 North LaSalle Street, Chicago 2, Illinois.

Distributes, in the form of Bulletins to members, information on improved methods of writing specifications for architectural and engineering materials, equipment and structures. Also publishes journal, SPECIFICATION RECORD.

American Society of Tool and Manufacturing Engineers, 10700 Puritan Avenue, Detroit, Michigan, 48238.

Conducts Creative Manufacturing Seminars in which papers on standards and standardization are frequently presented. Several examples are the following: Reed, E. A. DEVELOPMENT OF PRESSED METAL DIE STANDARDS.

Technical Paper SP63-28, October 1962. 23 p.
Hinkel, J. E. EVALUATION OF TODAY'S WELDING STANDARDS. Technical Paper SP63-63, January 1963. 16p.
Moyer, R. F. BASIC STANDARDS IN ELASTIC DIES. Technical Paper SP64-12, December 1963. 7 p.

American Standards Association, 10 East 40th Street, New York 16, New York.

1964 CATALOG OF AMERICAN STANDARDS. Annual. Includes a numerical listing, with prices of some 2500 American Standards. Additional lists in the catalog: Commercial Standards which have been approved by ASA; American Safety Standards; American Standards on Consumer Goods; an Organizational Cross Index to those American Standards that carry the designations of other organizations; Sales agents for American Standards in other countries; ASA special publications; Recommendations of the International Organization for Standardization; Recommendations of the International Electrotechnical Commission; and an index to titles of American Standards and International Recommendations.
CURRENT PROJECTS OF THE AMERICAN STANDARDS ASSOCIATION. Lists the 425 projects under which standards have been and are being developed and revised for presentation to ASA for approval as American Standards.
NATIONALLY RECOGNIZED STANDARDS IN STATE LAWS AND LOCAL ORDINANCES.
See 1964 Catalog of American Standards for additional publications of the ASA.
CATALOG OF SELECTED FOREIGN ELECTRICAL STANDARDS. List of national electrical standards issued by 38 foreign countries. O.P.
PROCEEDINGS OF THE NATIONAL CONFERENCES ON STANDARDS. Annual published proceedings which generally include several dozen papers on various aspects of standardization presented by representatives of industry, government, consumer groups, engineers, and scientists.
AVAILABLE INDEXES OF STANDARDS.
Lists indexes to standards issued by the national standardization bodies in 43 countries; to regional standards such as EURONORMS (Published by the European Montane Union and Administration of the European Coal and Steel Community), and INSTA (Inter-Nordic Standarziation).
Townsend, J. R. RECORD; ASA FROM 1948 TO 1962. MAGAZINE OF STANDARDS 32:357-360, December 1961.
Ainsworth, C. WHY ASA? Materials Research & Standards 3:492-493, June 1963.
Lamb, H. G. WHAT IS ASA? A SHORT HISTORY

OF THE AMERICAN STANDARDS ASSOCIATION. Magazine of Standards 33:180-181, June 1962.
Frost, F. C. WHAT IS ASA? PRINCIPLES AND CONCEPTS OF THE AMERICAN STANDARDS ASSOCIATION. Magazine of Standards 33:214-216, July 1962.
Hoffman, S. D. WHAT IS ASA? THE SECTIONAL COMMITTEE METHOD. Magazine of Standards 33:276-278, September 1962.
Hilton, C. E. WHAT IS ASA? THE EXISTING STANDARD AND THE GENERAL ACCEPTANCE METHODS--INCLUDING PROPRIETARY SPONSORSHIP. Magazine of Standards 33:310-312, October 1962.
Hussey, G. F. ASA STANDARDS LIBRARY...AT YOUR SERVICE. Standards Engineering 13:10-11, April-May 1961.

American Trucking Association, 1616 P Street, N.W., Washington 6, D.C.

RECOMMENDED EQUIPMENT SPECIFICATIONS:
E-1 ELECTRICAL CONNECTOR FOR TRUCK TRAILER JUMPER CABLE, INCLUDING CABLE PLUG, TRAILER SOCKET AND UNIFORM WIRING PATTERN.
E-2 REMOVABLE IDENTIFICATION SIGN FOR USE ON LEASED VEHICLES.
E-3 ELECTRICAL LIGHTING AND WIRING FOR COMMERCIAL VEHICLE BODIES.

American Vacuum Society, Office of the Secretary, 4 Old Salem Road, Marblehead, Massachusetts.

RECOMMENDED STANDARDS (TENTATIVE):
HELIUM MASS SPECTROMETER LEAK DETECTOR CALIBRATION.
METHOD FOR MEASURING SPEED OF OIL DIFFUSION PUMPS.
METHOD FOR MEASURING THROUGHOUT OF OIL DIFFUSION PUMPS.
METHODS FOR MEASURING THE FOREPRESSURE CHARACTERISTICS OF OIL DIFFUSION PUMPS.
METHOD FOR MEASURING BACKSTREAMING OF OIL DIFFUSION PUMPS.
MEASURE FOR MEASURING THE ULTIMATE PRESSURE OF PUMPS WITHOUT WORKING FLUIDS.
METHOD OF MEASURING SPEED OF PUMPS WITHOUT WORKING FLUIDS.
MEASUREMENT OF BLANK-OFF PRESSURE (PERMANENT GASES) OF POSITIVE DISPLACEMENT MECHANICAL VACUUM PUMPS.
PRESENTATION OF PUMPING SPEED CURVES OF MECHANICAL PUMPS.

American Water Works Association, 2 Park Avenue, New York 16, New York.

AWWA PUBLICATIONS lists over 60 Standards in the following series:
A - Source.
B - Treatment (filtration, softening, disinfection, coagulation, scale and corrosion control, taste and odor control, prophylaxis.
C - Distribution (cast-iron pipe, fittings; steel pipe; concrete pipe; asbestos-cement pipe; valves and hydrants; pipe-laying; meters; service line).
D - Storage.
E - Pumping.
STANDARD METHODS FOR THE EXAMINATION OF WATER AND WASTEWATER.
Prepared and published jointly with the American Public Health Association and the Water Pollution Control Federation.

American Welding Society, 345 East 47th Street, New York 17, New York.

PUBLICATIONS ORDER FORM lists over 60 standards:
Group A - Fundamentals of welding: definitions, symbols, testing; filler metal specifications; safety.
Group B - Inspection and qualification.
Group C - Processes: resistance welding; metallizing; brazing and soldering.
Group D - Industrial applications: automotive, bridges, building, piping, rockets, ships, storage tanks.
INDEX OF WELDING STANDARDS FROM 21 NATIONS.
Standards of each Nation are classified separately in French, English and the original language. Sources for addresses of the standards are given.
THE AWS BIBLIOGRAPHIES (1937-61).

American Wood-Preservers' Association, 389 Seventeenth Street, N.W., Washington 6, D.C.

AWPA MANUAL OF RECOMMENDED PRACTICE contains all current Association standards relating to preservatives, treatment of timber products, analysis and sampling of preservatives, and several miscellaneous standards.
Standards also available separately.

American Wood Preservers Institute, 111 West Washington Street, Chicago 2, Illinois.

MARINE WOOD PILES.
Booklet which incorporates Commercial Standards CS249-62, PRESSURE TREATED DOUGLAS FIR MARINE PILES, and Commercial Standard CS250-62 PRESSURE TREATED SOUTHERN PINE MARINE PILES.

Anti-Friction Bearing Manufacturers Association, 60 East 42nd Street, New York 17, New York.

STANDARDS BOOK.
Consists of 12 sections (in ring binder or available separately).
Section 1 - Terminology and nomenclature for various types of bearings and bearing parts.
Section 2 - Bearing boundary dimensions for all standard bearings.
Section 3 - Bearing tolerances for ball and roller bearings.
Section 4 - Gaging practices and definitions for bearing measurement, including radial internal clearance.
Section 5 - Bearing identification code.
Section 6 - Method of packaging bearings.
Section 7 - Bearing mounting for ball and roller bearings.
Section 8 - Mounting accessories--locknuts, washers and adapters.
Section 9 - Method for evaluating load ratings of radial ball bearings and thrust ball bearings.
Section 10 - Balls-terminology, definitions and tolerances.
Section 11 - Method for evaluating load ratings of radial roller bearings and thrust roller bearings.
Section 12 - Instrument ball bearings.

Architectural Aluminum Manufacturers Association, 35 East Wacker Drive, Chicago 1, Illinois.

AAMA 302.2 ALUMINUM WINDOW SPECIFICATIONS.
AAMA 404.2 ALUMINUM SLIDING DOORS SPECIFICATIONS.

Architectural Woodwork Institute, 332 South Michigan Avenue, Chicago 4, Illinois.

GUIDE SPECIFICATION FOR ARCHITECTURAL WOODWORK.
QUALITY STANDARDS OF THE ARCHITECTURAL WOODWORK INDUSTRY.
Includes lumber grades; plywood grades; standing and running trim; casework; panel work; closet and storage shelving; miscellaneous ornamental items; stairwork; exterior frames; exterior sash; screens; blinds and shutters; flush solid core doors; hollow core flush doors; stile and rail doors.

Asbestos Textile Institute, P.O. Box 239, 75 Center Street, Pompton Lakes, New Jersey.

HANDBOOK OF ASBESTOS TEXTILES.
In addition to information and data on asbestos and asbestos fibers and fabrics, there is a list of applicable

specifications and method of test of the American Society for Testing and Materials.

Asphalt and Vinyl Asbestos Tile Institute, 101 Park Avenue, New York 17, New York.
SPECIFICATIONS AND RECOMMENDATIONS on tile; adhesives; cleaners; wax; installation; and maintenance.

Asphalt Institute, Asphalt Institute Building, University of Maryland, College Park, Maryland.
SPECIFICATIONS AND CONSTRUCTIONS METHODS FOR HOT-MIX ASPHALT PAVING.
SPECIFICATIONS FOR ASPHALT CEMENTS.

Associated Cooperage Industries of America, 408 Olive Street, St. Louis 2, Missouri.
WOODEN BARREL MANUAL contains Interstate Commerce Commission Regulations: Shipping Container Specifications 11-A Wooden barrels and kegs, slack; and Shipping Container Specifications 10-A, 10-B, and 10-C Wooden barrels and kegs, tight.

Associated General Contractors of America, 1957 E Street, N.W., Washington 6, D.C.
CONTRACTORS PUMP STANDARDS.
CONCRETE MIXER STANDARDS.

Association for Computing Machinery, 211 East 43rd Street New York 17, New York.
Gorn, S. REITERATION OF ACM POLICY TOWARD STANDARDIZATION. Communications of the ACM 5:547-549, November 1962.
Kent, Eric R. A PROPOSAL FOR A SET OF PUBLICATION STANDARDS FOR USE BY THE ACM. Communications of the ACM 3:70-71, February 1960.

Association of American Battery Manufacturers, 19 North Harrison Street, East Orange, New Jersey.
BATTERY SPECIFICATIONS.

Association of American Railroads, Transportation Building, Washington 6, D.C.
PRICE LIST OF PUBLICATIONS lists many specifications and recommendations as well as the following major compilations:
STANDARD CODE OF OPERATING RULES, BLOCK SIGNAL RULES, INTERLOCKING RULES.
MANUAL OF RECOMMENDED PRACTICES (COMMUNICATION AND SIGNAL).

SPECIFICATIONS FOR COMMUNICATION AND SIGNAL WIRES AND CABLES.
A.R.E.A. MANUAL OF RECOMMENDED PRACTICES (CONSTRUCTION AND MAINTENANCE).
SPECIFICATIONS FOR STEEL RAILWAY BRIDGES.
SPECIFICATIONS FOR TANK CARS.
SPECIFICATIONS FOR MOVABLE RAILWAY BRIDGES.
A.A.R. MANUAL OF STANDARD AND RECOMMENDED PRACTICES (MECHANICAL).
A.A.R. ELECTRICAL MANUAL OF STANDARD AND RECOMMENDED PRACTICE.

Association of Casualty and Surety Companies, 110 William Street, New York 38, New York.
HANDBOOK OF INDUSTRIAL SAFETY STANDARDS.
"A compilation of industrial safety requirements... based on codes and recommendations of the American Standards Association, the National Fire Protection Association, American Society of Mechanical Engineers and various government agencies."

Association of Iron and Steel Engineers, 1010 Empire Building, Pittsburgh 22, Pa.
Standards for D-C Mill Motor; A-C Mill Motor; Machined Surfaces Finishes; Sling and Crane Chain; Wiring Diagrams; Electric Overhead Traveling Cranes for Steel Mill Service; Ladle Hooks; Hot Metal Ladles; D-C Mill Motor Brake; and Plain Bearing.

Association of Official Agricultural Chemists, Box 540 Benjamin Franklin Station, Washington 4, D.C.
OFFICIAL METHODS OF ANALYSIS OF THE AOAC.
INFRARED, ULTRAVIOLET, AND VISIBLE ABSORPTION SPECTRA OF SOME USP AND NF REFERENCE STANDARDS AND THEIR DERIVATIVES.

Association of Official Seed Analysts, 329 U.S. Court House, Kansas City, Missouri 64106.
RULES FOR TESTING SEEDS.

Association of Petroleum Re-Refiners, Box 7116, Arlington, Virginia.
CONTROL SPECIFICATIONS FOR ASSOCIATION OF PETROLEUM RE-REFINERS, SAE 10 to SAE 40 INCL.

Audio Engineering Society, P.O. Box 12, Old Chelsea Station, New York 11, New York.
AES DISK STANDARD.
AES: TSA-1-1954 A STANDARD PLAYBACK

CHARACTERISTIC FOR LATERAL DISK RECORDING.

Baking Industry Sanitation Standards Committee, 521 Fifth Avenue, New York 17, New York.

Distributes a list entitled STATUS OF SANITATION STANDARDS which has 23 standards on various types of bakery equipment and 14 pending standards.

Book Manufacturers' Institute, 25 West 43rd Street, New York, New York 10036.

OFFICIAL MINIMUM MANUFACTURING STANDARDS AND SPECIFICATIONS FOR TEXTBOOKS.
Co-sponsored by the National Association of State Textbook Directors and the American Textbook Publishers Institute.

Building Officials Conference of America, 1525 East 53rd Street, Chicago 15, Illinois.

BOCA BUILDING CODES.

Business Equipment Manufacturers Association, 235 East 42nd Street, New York 17, New York.

OFFICE MACHINES GROUP FACT SHEET, and ASA X3 AND BEMA/DPG, two publications which describe the Association's standardization activities.

California Redwood Association, 617 Montgomery Street, San Francisco 11, California.

STANDARD SPECIFICATIONS FOR GRADES OF CALIFORNIA REDWOOD LUMBER.
DATA SHEETS - PROPERTIES AND GRADES.
REDWOOD INSPECTION SERVICE GRADING RULES.
STANDARD PATTERNS - REDWOOD LUMBER.

Canvas Products Association-International, 224 Endicott Building, St. Paul 1, Minnesota.

CPAI-63 SPECIFICATION FOR CANVAS TARPAULINS, SINGLE FILLING FLAT DUCK ONLY.

Cast Iron Soil Pipe Institute, 205 West Wacker Drive, Chicago 6, Illinois.

WHY IT IS DESIRABLE TO SPECIFY A STANDARD FOR CAST IRON SOIL PIPE AND FITTINGS AND HOW TO SPECIFY THEM. Commercial Standard 188-59 CAST IRON SOIL PIPE AND FITTINGS.

Caster and Floor Truck Manufacturers' Association, 27 East Monroe Street, Chicago 3, Illinois.

ENGINEERING AND PURCHASING PLANBOOK lists and discusses standards for industrial wheels; hospital casters, wheels, and glide; industrial casters; two-wheel hand trucks; platform floor trucks; and tow line trucks.
Standards in the process of development by the Association include a polyurethane industrial wheel standard for manually operated equipment; a standard for low profile wheels and for demountable tired wheels.

Cemented Carbide Producers Association, 2130 Keith Building, Cleveland 15, Ohio.
STANDARDS DEVELOPED BY CEMENTED CARBIDE PRODUCERS ASSOCIATION is a listing which includes several standards approved as American Standards and several submitted for approval as American Standards.
Recommended Guides are: RECOMMENDED UNIFORM SYSTEM OF DESIGNATION FOR CEMENTED CARBIDE PRODUCTS.
RECOMMENDED GUIDE FOR CARBIDE RECTANGULAR STRIP.
RECOMMENDED METHOD OF CLASSIFICATION FOR CHIPS AND SIMILAR VOID TYPE DEFECTS.
RECOMMENDED GUIDE FOR SIZES OF BLANKS FOR CARBIDE TIPPED GUN DRILLS.
There is also one Simplified Practice Recommendation included, R263-60, STANDARD SHAPES, SIZES, GRADES, AND DESIGNATIONS OF CEMENTED CARBIDE PRODUCTS.

Chemical Specialties Manufacturers Association, 50 East 41st Street, New York 17, New York.
STANDARD REFERENCE TESTING MATERIALS for insecticides, brake fluids, corrosion, antifreeze corrosion, and floor waxes.

Chlorine Institute, 342 Madison Avenue, New York 17, New York
SPECIFICATIONS FOR CHLORINE SHIPPING CONTAINER VALVE PACKING.

Clay Flue Lining Institute, 161 Ash Street, Akron 8, Ohio.
RECOMMENDED BUILDING CODE TEXT FOR CHIMNEYS AND FLUES.

Clay Products Association, Box 172, Barrington, Illinois.
CLAY PIPE ENGINEERING MANUAL.
Chapter 15 of this manual contains Specifications and Standards for dimension of standard and extra-strength pipe and fittings. Chapter 16 is an Appendix containing American Society for Testing and Materials Specifications for standard and extra strength clay pipe; perforated

clay pipe; recommended practice for laying clay pipe; clay filter blocks; clay liner plates; and methods of test.

Compressed Air and Gas Institute, 122 East 42nd Street, New York 17, New York.

STANDARDS FOR CENTRIFUGAL AIR COMPRESSORS. Information on uncooled, single-stage and multistage centrifugal air compressors and accessories essential to satisfactory operation of such compressors.

STANDARD FOR PORTABLE PNEUMATIC TOOL NOISE MEASUREMENT.

Compressed Gas Association, 500 Fifth Avenue, New York 36, New York.

STANDARDS FOR WELDING AND BRAZING ON THIN WALLED CONTAINERS.

STANDARDS FOR VISUAL INSPECTION OF COMPRESSED GAS CYCLINDERS.

STANDARD FOR REQUALIFICATION OF IVV-3HT CYLINDERS.

STANDARDS FOR GASEOUS HYDROGEN SYSTEMS AT CONSUMER SITES.

TENTATIVE STANDARD FOR COMPRESSED AIR FOR HUMAN RESPIRATION.

STANDARD FOR MEDICAL VACUUM SYSTEMS IN HOSPITALS.

STANDARD FOR AMMONIUM NITRATE.

Also several standards on safety release devices.

Henderson, W. G. PROBLEMS ENCOUNTERED IN SPECIFYING PRESSURE VESSELS AND EQUIPMENT FOR USE IN VARIOUS STATES AND PROVINCES. Supplement to Fiftieth Annual Report, Compressed Gas Association, 1962, p.61-64.

Concrete Reinforcing Steel Institute, 228 North LaSalle Street, Chicago 1, Illinois.

REINFORCED CONCRETE -- A MANUAL OF STANDARD PRACTICE.

RECOMMENDED PRACTICE FOR PLACING REINFORCING BARS.

Construction Specifications Institute, 632 DuPont Circle Building, Washington 6, D.C.

MANUAL OF PRACTICE FOR SPECIFICATION WRITING METHODS (Tentative)

Outlines specification writing procedures which can be used on a national basis.

TECHNICAL STUDIES on various subjects, e.g., Gypsum Dry-Wall Construction; Ready-Mixed Concrete;

lathing and Plastering; Builders' Finishing Hardware, and many others. Each study includes data pertinent to specification writing and consists of the following:
Part I - Work Included. A check list of items customarily specified in the specification section under study.
Part II - Work Not Included. A check list of work customarily specified in other specification sections.
Part III - Specification Nomenclature.
Part IV - Bibliography. Important references including all applicable codes, local, state, regional, national, and industrial.
Part V - Discussion of Materials and Methods.
CONSTRUCTION SPECIFIER, monthly.
Part 2 of the June 1963 issue consists of THE CSI FORMAT FOR BUILDING SPECIFICATIONS.
An article on sheet metal specifications in Air Conditioning, Heating and Ventilation 60:8, June 1963 states that the Construction Specifications Institute will prepare specifications that clearly describe the work that shall be done <u>and</u> the performance expected of the installed equipment.

Conveyor Equipment Manufacturers Association, One Thomas Circle, Washington 5, D.C.
CONVEYOR TERMS AND DEFINITIONS.
CEMA STANDARD NO. 201 - 1960 KEYS, KEYSEATS & KEYWAYS.
CEMA STANDARD NO. 401 - 1962 ROLLER CONVEYORS - NON-POWERED.

Cooling Tower Institute, Suite 204 - 4242 Richmond Avenue, Houston, Texas 77027.
STD-103 REDWOOD LUMBER SPECIFICATIONS.
STD-111 GEAR SPEED REDUCERS.
STD-114 DOUGLAS FIR LUMBER SPECIFICATIONS (COAST TYPE).
STD-115 SOUTHERN PINE LUMBER SPECIFICATIONS.
STD-118 INQUIRY AND BID FORM.
STD-119 TIMBER FASTENER SPECIFICATIONS.
STD-201 CERTIFICATION STANDARD FOR COMMERCIAL WATER-COOLING TOWERS.
Hoffman, Paul R. COOLING TOWER INSTITUTE ANNOUNCES COMMERCIAL CERTIFICATION PROGRAM. Air Conditioning, Heating and Ventilating 61:88, March 1964.

Copper and Brass Research Association, 420 Lexington Avenue, New York 17, New York
STANDARDS MANUAL FOR COPPER AND COPPER ALLOY MILL PRODUCTS. "These standards apply to

wrought mill products of copper and copper alloys, including plate, sheet, strip, rod, bar, wire, pipe, tube and shapes (but not wire and cable of copper and copper alloy for electrical transmission)."

Crucible Manufacturers Association, 271 North Avenue, New Rochelle, New York.

CRUCIBLE MELTING HANDBOOK contains recommended standard sizes, dimensions and capacities of crucibles.

Diamond Core Drill Manufacturers Association, 122 East 42nd Street, New York 17, New York.

BULLETIN NO. 2 - STANDARDS OF THE DIAMOND CORE DRILL MANUFACTURERS ASSOCIATION. Designed to provide the purchaser with all the information needed to write a detailed specification for universally interchangeable diamond drilling equipment.

Diesel Engine Manufacturers Association, 122 East 42nd Street, New York 17, New York.

STANDARD PRACTICES FOR STATIONARY DIESEL AND GAS ENGINES.

Douglas Fir Plywood Association, 1119 A Street, Tacoma 2, Washington.

COMMERCIAL STANDARD CS 122-60 FOR WESTERN SOFTWOOD PLYWOOD.
COMMERCIAL STANDARD CS 45-60 FOR DOUGLAS FIR PLYWOOD.
PLYWOOD FOR TODAY'S CONSTRUCTION. Includes information on grades and suggested specifications.

Edison Electric Institute, 750 Third Avenue, New York 17, New York.

List of SUGGESTIONS FOR SPECIFICATIONS for materials and equipment used by electric companies. These are intended as information for the member companies in preparing their own purchase specifications for such items. About 60 specifications in all.

Elastic Fabric Manufacturers Institute, Box 710, New London, Connecticut.

WOVEN WAISTBAND ELASTIC--MINIMUM PERFORMANCE STANDARD.
BRAIDED WAISTBAND ELASTIC, QUALITY PERFORMANCE STANDARD A-1.

Electric Apparatus Service Association, 7730 Carondelet, St. Louis

5, Missouri
REWINDING STANDARDS - SINGLE PHASE INDUCTION MOTORS AND THREE PHASE INDUCTION MOTORS.
REBUILDING STANDARDS - TRANSFORMER.
REBUILDING STANDARDS - ELECTRIC MOTOR AND GENERATOR.

Electric Overhead Crane Institute, One Thomas Circle, Washington 5, D.C.
SPECIFICATION 61 - SPECIFICATIONS FOR ELECTRIC OVERHEAD TRAVELING CRANES.

Electronic Industries Association, Engineering Department, 11 West 42nd Street, New York 36, New York.
MANUAL OF ORGANIZATION AND PROCEDURE, Engineering Publication Ep-1B discusses standardization procedure. List of RECOMMENDED STANDARDS, SPECIFICATIONS AND ENGINEERING PUBLICATIONS, with Alphabetical Index. Included are some 200 standards on amplifiers, antennas, capacitors, cathode ray tubes, electron tubes, loudspeakers, magnetic recording equipment, phonograph components, printed wiring, resistors, semiconductor devices, television, and radio receivers, transmission lines, among others.
Caffiaux, J. A. ACCENTUATE THE POSITIVE; REORGANIZED COMPONENT PARTS STANDARDIZATION COMMITTEES. Magazine of Standards 31:144-147, May 1960.
Caffiaux, J. A. LOOK, MA--NO HANDS! A REVIEW OF EIA STANDARDIZATION ACTIVITIES IN THE FIELD OF NUMERICAL CONTROLS FOR MACHINE TOOLS. Magazine of Standards 33:373-375, December 1962.

Entomological Society of America, 4603 Calvert Road, College Park, Maryland.
PESTICIDE REFERENCE STANDARDS.

Expanded Shale, Clay and Slate Institute, National Press Building, Washington 4, D.C.
LIGHTWEIGHT CONCRETE INFORMATION SHEET NO. 11 - GUIDE SPECIFICATIONS FOR STRUCTURAL LIGHTWEIGHT CONCRETE.
LIGHTWEIGHT CONCRETE INFORMATION SHEET NO. 10 - CONCRETE MASONRY GUIDE SPECIFICATIONS.
Section 2 of the CONCRETE MASONRY MANUAL is a 3-page discussion of Suggested Specifications.

Expansion Joint Manufacturers Association, 53 Park Place,

New York 7, New York.
STANDARDS OF THE EXPANSION JOINT MANUFACTURERS ASSOCIATION.
Section 1 - Nomenclature.
Section 2 - Types of Expansion Joints and Their Basic Applications.
Section 3 - Movements, Forces, and Moments.
Section 4 - Use of Internal Sleeves in Expansion Joints.
Section 5 - Flanges.
Section 6 - Tie Rods, Hinges, and Similar Accessories.
Section 7 - Cycle Life Expectancy.
Section 8 - Corrosion.
Section 9 - Erosion.
Section 10 - Installation Instructions.

Facing Tile Institute, 1520 18th Street, N.W., Washington 6, D.C.
SPECIFICATIONS FOR GLAZED AND UNGLAZED STRUCTURAL FACING TILE.
SPECIFICATIONS FOR SELECT QUALITY CERAMIC GLAZE STRUCTURAL CLAY FACING TILE WITH SCR VERILITE AGGREGATE.
STRUCTURAL CLAY FACING TILE HANDBOOK.

Feedwater Heater Manufacturers Association, 53 Park Place, New York 7, New York.
STANDARDS OF FEEDWATER HEATER MANUFACTURERS ASSOCIATION.
Includes general standards, thermal standards, mechanical standards, standards on tubes, baffles and support plates, connections, tube sheets, channel covers, material standards, protection of heaters, maintenance, inspection and cleaning, workmanship, tolerances, and characteristics of tubing.

Flat Glass Jobbers Association, P.O. Box 677, Topeka, Kansas.
GLAZING MANUAL.
Includes specifications for sash, curtain walls, store fronts, flush glazing doors, glass veneer, and mirrors.

Fluid Controls Institute, P.O. Box 1485, Pampano Beach, Florida.
FCI 55-1 STANDARD CLASSIFICATION AND TERMINOLOGY FOR POWER ACTUATED VALVES.
FCI 58-1 DEFINITIONS OF REGULATOR CAPACITIES.
FC 58-2 RECOMMENDED VOLUNTARY STANDARDS FOR MEASUREMENT PROCEDURES FOR DETERMINING CONTROL VALVE FLOW CAPACITY.
FCI 61-1 RECOMMENDED VOLUNTARY STANDARDS FOR PROCEDURE IN RATING FLOW AND PRESSURE CHARACTERISTICS OF SOLENOID VALVES.
FCI 62-1 RECOMMENDED VOLUNTARY STANDARD FORMULAS FOR SIZING CONTROL VALVES.

Friction Materials Standards Institute, 370 Lexington Avenue, New York 17, New York.

AUTOMOTIVE BRAKE LINING AND CLUTCH FACING DATA BOOK. BRAKE SHOE IDENTIFICATION CATALOG contains compilations of standardized numbering systems assigned to the various sizes of brake linings, clutch facings and brake shoes installed as original equipment on passenger cars, trucks, busses, and trailers. BRAKE LINING STANDARDS BEING STUDIED BY FMSI. Gasoline Retailer 57:31, August 19, 1964.

Gas Vent Institute, 333 North Michigan Avenue, Chicago 1, Illinois.

GAS VENT CAPACITY TABLES.
Standard engineering method of sizing gas vents.

Gray Iron Founders' Society, National City-East Sixth Building, Cleveland 14, Ohio.

SUMMARY OF SPECIFICATIONS FOR GRAY CAST IRONS AND DUCTILE (NODULAR) CAST IRONS. Covers the more commonly used specifications and gives a list of the principal specifying groups.

Grinding Wheel Institute, 2130 Keith Building, Cleveland 15, Ohio.

Distributes several American Standards on abrasive and grinding wheels, diamond wheel shapes, abrasive discs and plate mounted wheels, and diamond grinding wheels. SPECIFICATIONS OF SEGMENTS USED IN CHUCKS. SAFETY RECOMMENDATIONS FOR GRINDING WHEEL OPERATION. Carndt, J. HOW GRINDING WHEEL INSTITUTE PROMOTES SAFETY Grinding & Finishing 9:38-39, March 1963.

Gummed Industries Association, 415 Lexington Avenue, New York 17, New York

GIA TEST BINDER.
Contains all specifications, standards and test methods on products of the industry.
GIA O1-59a CORRUGATORS BOX TAPE INDUSTRY SPECIFICATION.
Section I Glass Reinforced Tapes
Section II Sisal Reinforced Tapes
Section III Nylon Reinforced Tapes - One Ply
Section IV Paper Tapes
Section V Cambric and Clayfilled Cloth Tapes
Section VI Multi-ply Tapes

Hardwood Dimension Manufacturers Association, 3813 Hillsboro Road, Nashville 12, Tennessee.

STANDARDS AND GRADING RULES for the measurement and inspection of glued and solid dimension parts for furniture, industrial and other uses; hardwood interior trim and moldings; and hardwood stair treads and risers.

Hearing Aid Industry Conference, Valley Brook Road, Cannonsburg, Pennsylvania.

HAIC STANDARD METHOD OF EXPRESSING HEARING-AID PERFORMANCE.
STANDARDS FOR HEARING TESTING (IN PROCESS).

Heat Exchange Institute, 122 East 42nd Street, New York 17, New York.

STANDARDS AND TYPICAL SPECIFICATIONS FOR DEAERATORS AND DEAERATING HEATERS.
DIRECT CONTACT BAROMETRIC AND LOW LEVEL JET CONDENSER STANDARDS.
STEAM SURFACE CONDENSER STANDARDS.
TYPICAL SPECIFICATIONS FOR STEAM SURFACE CONDENSERS AND AUXILIARIES.
HISTORY OF THE DEVELOPMENT, MANUFACTURE AND CALIBRATION OF HEI FLOW NOZZLES.
METHOD AND PROCEDURE FOR THE DETERMINATION OF DISSOLVED OXYGEN.
STANDARDS FOR STEAM EJECTORS.

Hoist Manufacturers Association, One Thomas Circle, Washington 5, D.C.

STANDARD SPECIFICATIONS FOR MANUALLY OPERATED HOISTS.
STANDARD SPECIFICATIONS FOR HAND OPERATED HOISTS.
STANDARD SPECIFICATIONS FOR ELECTRIC WIRE ROPE HOISTS.
STANDARD SPECIFICATIONS FOR ELECTRIC CHAIN HOISTS.

Hydraulic Institute, 122 East 42nd Street, New York 17, New York.

STANDARDS OF THE HYDRAULIC INSTITUTE, with 1st, 2nd, and 3rd revisions.
Gives data on centrifugal, rotary and reciprocating pumps, including terminology, hydraulic standards, methods of test, installation, and operation.

Illuminating Engineering Society, 345 East 47th Street, New York 17, New York.

I.E.S. RECOMMENDED LIGHTING PRACTICES:
RP - 1 Office Lighting
RP - 3 School Lighting
RP - 30 School Lighting Application Data

RP - 4 Library Lighting
RP - 5 Daylighting
RP - 6 Sports Lighting
RP - 9 Supplementary Lighting
RP - 10 Protective Lighting
RP - 11 Residence Lighting
RP - 12 Marine Lighting
RP - 13 Outdoor Parking Area Lighting
RP - 14 Airport Service Area Lighting
RP - 15 Recommended Levels of Illumination

I.E.S. LIGHTING HANDBOOK contains recommended minimum footcandles for every task.
I.E.S. COMMITTEE REPORTS - Lighting recommendations based upon studies of I.E.S. committees and subcommittees covering all phases of lighting.
MEASUREMENT AND TESTING GUIDES.

Incinerator Institute of America, 630 Third Avenue, New York 17, New York.
I.I.A. INCINERATOR STANDARDS.

Indiana Limestone Institute, Bedford, Indiana.
AMERICAN STANDARDS SPECIFICATIONS FOR INDIANA LIMESTONE, ASA A93.1-1948.

Industrial Diamond Association of America, 587A Turnpike, Pompton Plains, New Jersey.
AMERICAN STANDARD B 67.1 DIAMOND DRESSING TOOLS, co-sponsored with the American Society of Tool & Manufacturing Engineers.
AMERICAN STANDARD B74-1 IDENTIFICATION CODE FOR DIAMOND WHEEL SHAPES, co-sponsored with Grinding Wheel Institute, cooperated in drawing up other American Standards and Commercial Standards.

Industrial Fasteners Institute, 1517 Terminal Tower, Cleveland 13, Ohio.
SPECIFICATIONS FOR STRUCTURAL JOINTS USING ASTM A325 BOLTS.
SPECIFICATIONS FOR HEXAGON LOCKNUTS, PREVAILING TORQUE-TYPE STEEL.
ENGINEERING RECOMMENDATION NO. 1 - That pan head machine and tapping screws be used instead of round, truss and binding head machine and tapping screws in the design of all new engineering assemblies.
IDENTIFICATION MARKINGS FOR FASTENERS. Fasteners 19:4-38, Spring 1964.
Special issue of the Institute's quarterly journal. Section I - Grade and Material Markings - lists the markings required by all nationally recognized specifica-

tions which are issued by the American Society for Testing and Materials, the Society of Automotive Engineers, Federal and Military specifications and those of the National Aerospace Committee.
Section II - Manufacturer Identification Symbols - lists the company identification symbols of American fastener manufacturers.
Subsequently issued as a 40-page manual bearing same title.
The Institute also issues ENGINEERING RECOMMENDATIONS in which existing standards, such as ASA and SAE are cited as the basis for the specific recommendation.

Industrial Gas Cleaning Institute, 420 Lexington Avenue, New York 17, New York.
SPECIFICATION-FABRIC DIVISION NO. 1 - FACTORS AFFECTING THE SELECTION OF FABRIC TYPE DUST COLLECTORS.
SPECIFICATION-ELECTROSTATIC PRECIPITATORS DIVISION NO. 1 - TERMINOLOGY FOR ELECTROSTATIC PRECIPITATORS.
In process are test procedures for gas scrubbers and several others.

Institute of Boiler and Radiator Manufacturers, 608 Fifth Avenue, New York 20, New York.
I=B=R CALCULATION GUIDES
I=B=R INSTALLATION GUIDES
I=B=R PIPING GUIDES
I=B=R CALCULATION SHEETS
I=B=R BASEBOARD RATINGS

Institute of Electrical and Electronics Engineers, 345 East 47th Street, New York 17, New York.
STANDARDS PUBLICATIONS SOLD BY THE INSTITUTE OF ELECTRICAL AND ELECTRONICS ENGINEERS.
This price list includes definitions, standards, methods of measurement, test procedures, recommended practices, specifications and guides, including certain American Standards and Test Codes. Due to the merger of the two organizations, all former standards of the American Institute of Electrical Engineers and of the Institute of Radio Engineers now have an IEEE designation. 275 documents are listed, and cover a very broad range of electrical and electronic equipment.
HOW WE USE ASA PROCEDURES. Magazine of Standards 35:103-104, April 1964.

Institute of Food Technologists, Suite 1350, 176 West Adams

Street, Chicago, Illinois. 60603

The annual meeting of the IFT, held in Washington, D.C., May 26-27, 1964, included several symposia on food standards. Some or all of the papers listed below are likely to appear in future issues of FOOD TECHNOLOGY, monthly journal of the Institute:

Monday, May 25 - General Session - Symposium - International Food Standards.

Introduction to International Food Standards. J. L. Harvey.

Codex Alimentarius. O. Hogl.

Food Chemicals Codex. J. L. Powers.

Standards of Identity and Wholesomeness. E. Abramson.

Technical Section 1A - Symposium - International Food Standards.

Problems With Plant Products. R. Allen.

Problems With Animal Products. M. H. Jul.

Standards of Quality. N. Koenig.

Problems of Transhipments. W. Pilnik.

Problems of Fareastern Countries. V. Subrahamanyan.

Problems of Mideastern Countries. G. Zimmerman.

Problems of East-European Countries. D. Sulc.

Problems of West-European Countries. E. Benk.

Problems of Exporting to America. R. A. Chapman.

Problems of Exporting From America. F. Elliott.

Section 2A1 - Sympsoium - U.S. Food Standards.

Food Standards and the FDA. M. R. Stephens.

Food Standards as Viewed by a State Food and Drug Official. V. E. Stewart.

Food Standards from the Viewpoint of the Baking and Frozen Food Industries. R. H. Cotton.

An Industry View of Food Standards. J. W. Bell and C. A. Greenleaf.

Institute of High Fidelity Manufacturers, 516 Fifth Avenue, New York 36, New York.

IHFM STANDARD METHODS OF MEASUREMENT FOR TUNERS.

IHFM STANDARD METHOD OF MEASUREMENT FOR AMPLIFIERS.

Institute of Printed Circuits, 27 East Monroe Street, Chicago 3, Illinois.

HOW TO DESIGN AND SPECIFY PRINTED CIRCUITS. Revision in process in looseleaf form.

Institutional Research Council, 221 West 57th Street, New York 19, New York.

WORKBOOK OF TEST METHODS AND STANDARDS FOR THE CERTIFIED PRODUCTS PROGRAM OF THE INSTITUTIONAL RESEARCH COUNCIL.

Includes specifications for abrasive cleaners; bowl and porcelain cleaners; hand and machine dishwashing compounds; floor cleaners; furniture, floor, and metal polishes; glass cleaner; wax stripper; paints; moth-proofing compounds; anti-bacterial compounds; commercial carpets; general purpose cleaners.

Instrument Society of America, Penn-Sheraton Hotel, 530 William Penn Place, Pittsburgh 19, Pennsylvania.

STANDARDS AND PRACTICES FOR INSTRUMENTATION. Contains 26 complete ISA Recommended Practices; 300 instrumentation standards and practices abstracted from those of 19 societies, the U.S. Government, the Canadian Standards Association, and the British Standards Institute. Title, identification number, issue date, and brief description for each instrumentation standard and practice is given as well as the name and address of the organization from which to order.
ISA TRANSDUCER COMPENDIUM.
RECOMMENDED PRACTICES.
INSTRUMENTATION SPECIFICATION FORM PADS.
MEASUREMENT STANDARDS INSTRUMENTATION, PREPRINT COMPILATION, ANNUAL CONFERENCE, NEW YORK, 1962. 26 papers.
MEASUREMENT STANDARDS REPORT, 1961. A 38-page ISA JOURNAL reprint which gives "a brief history of measurement, its importance in today's technology. Discusses the National Bureau of Standards, accuracy and evaluation of standards, standards laboratories, and the refining of measurements by capacitance techniques."
Linebrink, O. ROLE OF ISA IN MEASUREMENT STANDARDS. ISA Journal 8:69-70, February 1961.

International Association of Ice Cream Manufacturers, 1105 Barr Building, Washington, D.C.

DIGEST OF STATE LAWS AFFECTING ICE CREAM AND RELATED PRODUCTS.
A 1962 compilation which includes the standards established by each state, as well as labeling, packaging, sanitation and other requirements.

International Conference of Building Officials, 50 South Los Robles, Pasadena, California.

1964 editions of UNIFORM BUILDING CODES, VOLUMES I, II, and III.
UNIFORM BUILDING CODES SHORT FORM.
UNIFORM SIGN CODE.
UNIFORM HOUSING CODE.
BUILDING STANDARDS MONTHLY (journal).

Internal Combustion Engine Institute, 201 North Wells Street,

Chicago 6, Illinois.
GASOLINE ENGINE & POWER UNIT TEST CODE.

Insulation Board Institute, 111 West Washington Street, Chicago 2, Illinois.
RECOMMENDED PRODUCT AND APPLICATION SPECIFICATIONS.
IBI SPEC. NO. 1 - STRUCTURAL INSULATING ROOF DECK.
IBI SPEC. NO. 2 - 1/2 INCH FIBERBOARD NAIL-BASE SHEATHING.
IBI SPEC. NO. 3 - 1/2 INCH INTERMEDIATE FIBERBOARD SHEATHING.

Library Binding Institute, 160 State Street, Boston 9, Massachusetts.
STANDARD FOR LIBRARY BINDING.
Includes manufacturing and materials specifications.

Liquefied Petroleum Gas Association, 11 South LaSalle Street, Chicago 3, Illinois.
LP-GAS SERVICE TRAINING COURSE BOOK I - The Product, Standards and Regulations, Customer Relations. Includes chapters on the "why" and "how" of standards; a table of standards--a list, with brief descriptions, of applicable standards, practices and codes issued by 17 other organizations.
STANDARDS FOR THE USE OF LP-GAS IN FAMILY FALLOUT SHELTERS.

Magnetic Recording Industry Association, 110 North Wacker Drive, Chicago, Illinois.
PROGRESS REPORT OF THE STANDARDS COMMITTEE, May 17, 1963 has appended to it a list of existing magnetic standards of various trade and technical associations.

Manufacturers Standardization Society of the Valve and Fittings Industry, 420 Lexington Avenue, New York 17, New York.
PRICE LIST OF MSS STANDARD PRACTICES.
26 Standard Practices on valves, fittings, flanges, unions, castings, pipe hangers and supports, elbows, and other items are included. A large number of MSS Standard Practices have been approved as American Standards.

Manufacturing Chemists' Association, 1825 Connecticut Avenue, N.W., Washington 9, D.C.
MANUAL OF STANDARD AND RECOMMENDED PRACTICE for chemicals, containers, tank car unloading and related procedures.

Maple Flooring Manufacturers Association, 35 East Wacker Drive, Chicago 1, Illinois.

SPECIFICATION MANUAL - NORTHERN HARD MAPLE, BEECH AND BIRCH FLOORING.
GRADING RULES FOR NORTHERN HARD MAPLE, BEECH AND BIRCH FLOORING.

Mechanical Contractors Association of America, 666 Third Avenue New York 17, New York.

ENGINEERING STANDARDS.
Part 1 - Heat Loss calculations.
Part 2 - Net load recommendations; heating boilers, baseboard convectors, finned-tube; testing and rating codes for boiler-burner units.
Part 3 - Pipe sizes and design.
Part 4 - Comfort air conditioning.
Part 5 - Graphic symbols for use on drawings and scheme for identification of piping systems.
Part 6 - Panel heating.
Part 7 - Standard procedure specifications for welding of pipe, fittings and flanges.
Part 8 - Residential air conditioning.

Metal Cutting Tool Institute, 405 Lexington Avenue, New York 17, New York.

METAL CUTTING TOOL NOMENCLATURE.
STANDARDS AND DIMENSIONS FOR TAPS AND DIES.

Metal Lath Association, Engineers Building, Cleveland 14, Ohio.

SPECIFICATIONS FOR METAL LATHING AND FURRING.

Metal Powder Industries Federation, 60 East 42nd Street, New York 17, New York.

POWDER METALLURGY PUBLICATIONS LIST - Standards and Specifications and other Technical Publications for Metal Powders, Powder Metallurgy Parts, Oil-Impregnated Bearings, Metal Powder Cores, Ferrite Cores, and Powder Metallurgy Processing Equipment. The listed standards are of those associations which are members of the Federation, viz., Metal Powder Producers Association, Powder Metallurgy Parts Manufacturers Association, Magnetic Powder Core Association, and Powder Metallurgy Equipment Association.

Mobile Homes Manufacturers Association, 20 North Wacker Drive, Chicago 6, Illinois.

A119.1-1963 - AMERICAN STANDARDS INSTALLATIONS OF PLUMBING, HEATING, AND ELECTRICAL SYSTEMS IN MOBILE HOMES.
A119.2-1963 - AMERICAN STANDARDS INSTALLATIONS

OF PLUMBING, HEATING AND ELECTRICAL SYSTEMS IN TRAVEL TRAILERS.
According to the Magazine of Standards for September 1964, a subcommittee of the Mobile Homes Manufacturers Association has completed work leading to MHMA standards for body and frame design, with the draft proposal to be voted on sometime in 1965.

Modular Building Standards Association, 2029 K Street, N.W., Washington 6, D.C.
SELECTED LIST OF PUBLICATIONS PERTAINING TO MODULAR PRACTICES.
The list includes the following publications:
MODULAR PRACTICES IN BUILDING.
MODULAR DRAFTING MANUAL.
CURRENT STATUS OF MODULAR COORDINATION.
Summary of Research Correlation Conference which includes a review of modular standards.
ARCHITECTURAL GRAPHIC STANDARDS.
Also listed are several American Standards pertaining the manufactured sizes of materials to yield modular units.

National Association of Architectural Metal Manufacturers, 228 North LaSalle Street, Chicago 1, Illinois.
RECOMMENDATIONS CONCERNING HARDWARE FOR ALUMINUM DOORS.
FINISHES AND FINISHING STANDARDS REPORT.
Specification and design data on metal finishes for store fronts and entrances.

National Association of Broadcasters, 1771 N Street, N.W., Washington 6, D.C.
Issues standards on magnetic tape which are being updated. The standards deal with disc, reel-to-reel, and cartridge tape.
Bubbers, J. J. REPORT ON THE PROPOSED NAB DISC PLAYBACK STANDARD. Journal of the Audio Engineering Society 12:51-54, January 1964.

National Association of Building Owners and Managers, 134 South LaSalle Street, Chicago 3, Illinois.
STANDARD SYSTEM OF ACCOUNTING FOR OFFICE BUILDINGS.
STANDARD METHOD OF FLOOR MEASUREMENT FOR OFFICE BUILDINGS.
THE SHERIDAN-KARKOW FORMULA, A SUGGESTED STANDARD FOR DETERMINING RELATIVE RENTAL VALUES FOR VARIOUS SPACE LOCATIONS WITHIN

AN OFFICE BUILDING.
THE GILBERT FORMULA, A STANDARD FOR OFFICE BUILDING CLEANING.

National Association of Corrosion Engineers, 1061 M & M Building, Houston 2, Texas.

ISSUES TECHNICAL REPORTS, some of which are standards, specifications, or recommended practices. Examples of each are:
SPECIFICATIONS FOR ASBESTOS PIPELINE FELT.
SPECIFICATIONS FOR BITUMINOUS SATURATED GLASS PIPE WRAP.
RECOMMENDED PRACTICES APPLICABLE TO PLACING CEMENT LININGS IN OIL FIELD STEEL TUBULAR GOODS.
PROPOSED STANDARDIZED LABORATORY SCREENING TEST FOR MATERIALS TO BE USED AS INHIBITORS IN SOUR OIL AND GAS WELLS.
TENTATIVE STANDARD METHOD FOR MEASURING ELECTRICAL CONDUCTANCE OF COATING ON BURIED PIPE LINES.

National Association of Frozen Food Packers, 919 18th Street, N.W. Washington 6, D.C.

AFDOUS-NAFFP METHODOLOGY FOR MICROBIOLOGICAL TESTING OF PREPARED FROZEN FOODS.
FIVE STEPS TO SANITARY QUALITY OF FROZEN FOODS.
Contains literature references to standards for inspection and testing.
OFFICIAL PROCEDURE FOR CHECKING FROZEN FOOD NET WEIGHTS.

National Association of Furniture Manufacturers, Room 1721, 666 Lake Shore Drive, Chicago 11, IIllnois.

APPROVED SPECIFICATIONS OR MINIMUM STANDARDS FOR UPHOLSTERY FABRICS.
TESTS AND LIMITS FOR FURNITURE UPHOLSTERY FABRICS.

National Association of Hosiery Manufacturers, 468 Park Avenue South, New York 16, New York.

STANDARDS FOR WOMEN'S HOSIERY MADE OF MONOFILAMENT STRETCH YARN.
STANDARDS OF SPECIFICATION FOR NYLON STOCKINGS FOR WOMEN.

National Association of Plastic Fabricators, 1108 Standard Building, Cleveland 13, Ohio.

QUALITY SPECIFICATIONS FOR HIGH PRESSURE DECORATIVE LAMINATED PLASTIC PRODUCTS.

National Association of Purchasing Agents, 11 Park Place, New York 7, New York.

STANDARDIZATION MANUAL; A BOOK OF PRINCIPLES AND PRACTICES FOR PURCHASING PERSONNEL.
Section 1. Basic facts and definitions.
Section 2. Starting a standardization program in a company.
Section 3. The purchasing agent and standardization.
Section 4. Putting material standardization to work in the company.
Section 5. The status of the National Association of Purchasing Agents in national standardization.
Section 6. The American Standards Association.
Section 7. Sources of nationally recognized standards and standardization information.
A bibliography includes a list of talks and addresses on standardization, and books, articles and reprints on standardization.

National Association of Relay Manufacturers, P.O. Box 7765, Phoenix, Arizona.

RECOMMENDED SPECIFICATIONS FOR HIGH RELIABILITY RELAYS.

National Association of Secondary Material Industries, 271 Madison Avenue, New York 16, New York.

CIRCULAR CR-50 COTTON RAG SPECIFICATIONS.
CIRCULAR PS-63 PAPER STOCK STANDARDS AND PRACTICES.
CIRCULAR NF-58 STANDARD CLASSIFICATION FOR NONFERROUS SCRAP METALS.

National Association of State Purchasing Officials, The Council of State Governments, Secretariat, 1313 East 60th Street, Chicago 37, Illinois.

REPORTS ON FEDERAL SPECIFICATIONS.
Issued during the years 1956-1959. The Committee on Standardization of Specifications reviewed Federal specifications on selected commodities and reported those which might be adapted to state use. More than 3000 such reports were issued in 28 groups and distributed to all state purchasing officials.

INDEX OF STATE SPECIFICATIONS ON COMMODITIES, 1963.
An alphabetical listing of over 1500 commodities. For each commodity is indicated the existence of one or more specifications and the states making use of the specifications. Specification sources are Federal and Military Specifications, American Standards Association, American Society for Testing and Materials, the U.S.

Department of Agriculture, the Society of Automotive Engineers, Underwriters' Laboratories, the U.S. Department of Commerce, the U.S. Department of the Interior, the American Association of State Highway Officials, the American Association of Battery Manufacturers Association, the American Chemical Society, and the specifications of various states. A half dozen specifications of the U.S. Fish and Wildlife Service on fish fillets, scallops, and shrimp also bear NASPO designations.

National Association of Wiping Cloth Manufacturers, 173 West Madison Street, Chicago 2, Illinois.

SPECIFICATIONS FOR STERILIZED WIPING CLOTHS.
SPECIFICATIONS FOR PURCHASE OF RAGS FOR CONVERSION INTO WIPING CLOTHS.

National Audio-Visual Association, 1201 Spring Street, Fairfax, Virginia.

STANDARD SPECIFICATIONS FOR 35MM SINGLE FRAME FILMSTRIPS.

National Automatic Merchandising Association, 7 South Dearborn Street, Chicago 3, Illinois.

VENDING MACHINE EVALUATION MANUAL.
WATER HEATER SAFETY MANUAL FOR THE OPERATOR OF HOT BEVERAGE VENDING MACHINES.

National Board of Boiler and Pressure Vessel Inspectors, 1155 North High Street, Columbus 1, Ohio.

NATIONAL BOARD INSPECTION CODE.

National Board of Fire Underwriters, 85 John Street, New York 38, New York.

STANDARDS AND RECOMMENDED SAFEGUARDS for Fire Extinguishing Appliances; Fire Extinguishing Auxiliaries; Flammable Liquids; Combustible Solids; Gases; Explosive Dust; Electrical Equipment; Construction; and Transportation.

National Builders' Hardware Association, 515 Madison Avenue, New York 22, New York.

A115 AMERICAN STANDARD SPECIFICATIONS FOR DOOR AND FRAME PREPARATION FOR DOOR LOCKS AND FLUSH BOLTS.
ABBREVIATIONS AND SYMBOLS AS USED IN BUILDERS' HARDWARE SCHEDULES AND SPECIFICATIONS.
RECOMMENDED PROCEDURE FOR PROCESSING HARDWARE SCHEDULES AND TEMPLATES.

RECOMMENDATIONS CONCERNING HARDWARE FOR ALUMINUM DOORS.
HARDWARE FOR HOUSING.
Lists hardware for typical openings in various types of residential buildings, including minimum standard recommendations for public housing.
HARDWARE FOR LABELLED FIR DOORS.
Contains industry standards covering hardware for hinged fire doors carrying labels A to E of the Underwriters' Laboratories, Inc.

National Certified Pipe Welding Bureau, Suite 1464, 666 Third Avenue, New York 17, New York.
Procedure specifications of this Bureau are published by the Mechanical Contractors Association in Part 7 of its ENGINEERING STANDARDS. The eight procedure specifications cover several methods of welding steel pipe, valves, fittings and flanges made of various types of steel and steel alloys.

National Coal Association, 1130 Seventeenth Street, N.W., Washington 6, D.C.
GUIDE SPECIFICATIONS include:
GS-1 UNDERFEED STOKER-FIRED LOW PRESSURE HEATING PLANTS.
GS-2 UNDERFEED STOKER-FIRED INDUSTRIAL PLANT.
GS-3 TYPICAL APPLICATION OF COAL-PAK AUTOMATIC BOILER.
GS-4 COAL STOKER-FIRED STEAM PLANTS.

National Combination Storm Window & Door Institute, 280 Madison Avenue, New York 16, New York.
STANDARDS AND SPECIFICATIONS WITH TEST PROCEDURES.

National Concrete Masonry Association, 1015 Wisconsin Avenue, N.W., Washington 7, D.C.
SUGGESTED SPECIFICATIONS FOR CONCRETE MASONRY UNITS, MORTAR AND GROUT.
GUIDE SPECIFICATION FOR CONCRETE MASONRY.
BUILDING CODE REQUIREMENTS FOR MASONRY.
BUILDING CODE REQUIREMENTS FOR REINFORCED MASONRY.
STANDARD SIZES OF MODULAR MASONRY UNITS.

National Conference of Standards Laboratories, National Bureau of Standards, Boulder, Colorado.
PROCEEDINGS OF THE 1962 STANDARDS LABORATORY CONFERENCE.
The Conference, under the aegis of the National

Bureau of Standards, was organized in 1961 and brought together representatives of measurements standards and calibration laboratories to encourage, promote and achieve cooperative action on common problems of management and operation of measurement standards and calibration laboratories. These proceedings of a first conference present over thirty papers and summaries of panel discussions on a broad range of measurement standards problems. The program of the second conference of the National Conference of Standards Laboratories was integrated into the 19th Annual ISA Instrument-Automation Conference of the Instrument Society of American held October 12-15, 1964 in New York City.

A broad cross-section of papers on measurement standards were included in this program. Some of the session topics; Reliability Standards; Electrical Measurement Standards; The Mission of the National Standards Laboratories; Flow Instrumentation Standards; Calibration Practices; Microwave Standards; Standards Laboratory and Instrumentation Information Services; High Frequency Standards.

National Electrical Manufacturers Association, 155 East 44th Street, New York 17, New York.

ENGINEERING BULLETIN No. 24 - STANDARDIZATION ACTIVITIES OF THE NATIONAL ELECTRICAL MANUFACTURERS ASSOCIATION.

STANDARDS PUBLICATIONS.

This is a catalog and price list of over 200 standards for industrial and consumer products, such as capacitors, circuit breakers, automatic temperature controls, generating and converting apparatus, laminated thermosetting products, panelboards, rectifier units, semiconductor rectifier components and equipment, signalling apparatus, street and highway lighting, switches and switchgear, transformers, turbines, electric arc welding, wires and cable. Consumer product standards include those for room air conditioners, dehumidifiers, electric bedcoverings, coffeemakers, refrigerators, fans, freezers, and ranges.

ELECTRICAL INDUSTRY STANDARDS - TOOLS FOR PROGRESS.

A booklet summarizing the conclusions arrived at after a review of the standards and standardization activities of NEMA.

National Fibre Can and Tube Association, 1725 Eye Street, N.W., Washington 6, D.C.

NFCTA STANDARD TESTING PROCEDURES.

A dozen standards with others under development

covering dimensions and physical characteristics, such as dimensional stability and strength characteristics for fibre cans, tubes and cores.

National Fire Protection Association, 60 Batterymarch Street, Boston 10, Massachusetts.

NATIONAL FIRE CODES. Issued in seven volumes:
Volume I. Flammable liquids and gases. 33 standards.
Volume II. Combustible solids, dusts, chemicals, and explosives. 39 Standards.
Volume III. Building construction and equipment. 35 Standards.
Volume IV. Fixed extinguishing equipment. 20 Standards.
Volume V. Electrical. 11 Standards.
Volume VI. Transportation. 31 Standards.
Volume VII. Mobile fire equipment; organization and management. 24 Standards.

National Flexible Packaging Association, 11750 Shaker Boulevard, Cleveland 20, Ohio.

15 Specifications on converted cellophane and polyethlene film packaging materials that are flexographic and rotogravure printed, as well as unprinted.

National Fluid Power Association, P.O. Box 49, Thiensville, Wisconsin.

GLOSSARY OF TERMS FOR FLUID POWER.
CYLINDER DIMENSION IDENTIFICATION CODE.
RECOMMENDED ROD AND BORE SIZES FOR FLUID POWER CYLINDERS.
ACCUMULATOR CODE FOR FLUID POWER ACCUMULATORS.
METHODS OF RATING AND DUTY CLASSIFICATION FOR FLUID POWER PUMPS AND MOTORS.
HYDRAULIC FILTRATION STANDARDS FOR FLUID POWER SYSTEMS.
STANDARDS FOR SEALING DEVICES.
IDENTIFICATION OF PORTS AND LEADS FOR SOLENOID VALVES.
INTERCHANGEABLE DIMENSIONS FOR FLUID POWER CYCLINDERS.
PROCEDURES FOR THE USE OF FIRE RESISTANT FLUIDS.

National Hardwood Lumber Association, 59 East Van Buren Street, Chicago 5, Illinois.

RULES FOR THE MEASUREMENT AND INSPECTION OF HARDWOOD LUMBER, CYPRESS VENEERS, AND THIN LUMBER.

National Hose Assemblies Manufacturers Association, 53 Park Place, New York 7, New York.

SAFETY CODE FOR THE USE AND HANDLING OF HOSE AND HOSE ASSEMBLIES.

National Institute of Governmental Purchasing, 1001 Connecticut Avenue, N.W., Washington, D.C.

The Institute maintains for member use an extensive file of specifications and standards solicited from the purchasing agents of cities, states, provinces and municipalities, and from various government and other agencies. Its LETTER SERVICE to members lists these newly acquired documents as well as other publications and notes relative to standards and specifications developments.

National Institute of Jig and Fixture Component Manufacturers, 294 Fairmont Avenue, Oakland 11, California.

NATIONAL INSTITUTE OF JIG AND FIXTURE COMPONENT MANUFACTURERS STANDARDS. Machinery 69:143-144, February 1963.

National Lime Association, 925 Fifteenth Street, N.W., Washington 5, D.C.

SPECIFICATIONS FOR LIME AND ITS USE IN PLASTERING, STUCCO, UNIT MASONRY, AND CONCRETE.
PUBLICATION 4i Na. Lime, Masonry, Mortar, Plaster, Stucco. Includes technical data on mortar specifications and preparation, mortar recommendations, and stucco recommendations.

National Lumber Manufacturers Association, 1619 Massachusetts Avenue, N.W., Washington 6, D.C.

LUMBER AND WOOD PRODUCTS LITERATURE.
A catalog of publications available from 21 wood and wood products associations federated with the NLMA, as well as from 24 other organizations. The list is arranged under six major divisions incorporating 36 categories, two of which are "Grades, Grade Marking and Specifications" and "Grading Rules." Publications on standards, specifications and grades are also listed under other headings.
NATIONAL DESIGN SPECIFICATION FOR STRESS-GRADE LUMBER AND ITS FASTENINGS.
MAXIMUM SPANS FOR JOISTS AND RAFTERS IN RESIDENTIAL CONSTRUCTION.

National Machine Tool Builders' Association, 2139 Wisconsin Avenue, Washington 7, D.C.

MACHINE TOOL ELECTRICAL STANDARDS.

National Metal Awning Association, 280 Madison Avenue, New York 16, New York.
MINIMUM SPECIFICATIONS AND STANDARDS FOR METAL AWNINGS AND COVERS.

National Microfilm Association, P.O. Box 386, Annapolis, Maryland.
BASIC DoD SPECIFICATIONS AND STANDARDS - NMA INFORMATIONAL MONOGRAPH NO. 1.
A compilation of basic Department of Defense standards and specifications which are in effect for contract and other microfilm work undertaken by the DoD.
Hatfield, M.R. STANDARDS CHALLENGE TO THE NMA. Proceedings of the National Microfilm Association, 1963, pp. 63-66.

National Mineral Wool Insulation Association, 1270 Sixth Avenue, New York 20, New York.
THERMAL PERFORMANCE STANDARD MINERAL WOOL BUILDING INSULATION.
STANDARD FOR MINERAL WOOL BUILDING INSULATION.
NATIONAL MINERAL WOOL ASSOCIATION ADOPTS PERFORMANCE STANDARDS FOR HOUSE INSULATION. Air Conditioning, Heating and Refrigeration News 90:18-19, May 16, 1960.

National Oak Flooring Manufacturers' Association, 814 Sterick Building, Memphis, Tennessee.
OFFICIAL FLOORING GRADING RULES - OAK, PECAN, BEECH, BIRCH, HARD MAPLE.
SPECIFICATION MANUAL - N.O.F.M.A. CERTIFIED OAK FLOORS-PREPARATION, LAYING, FINISHING.

National Office Management Association, Willow Grove, Pennsylvania.
OFFICE STANDARDS.
A list of 21 standards being processed as American Standards. Include specifications for paper, bank checks, printing of business forms, adding machine paper rolls, carbon paper. Also standards for dimensions of desks and tables for general office use, installation of telephone equipment on desks, posture chair definitions, office lighting practices, office space assignments, and others.

National Paint, Varnish and Lacquer Association, 1500 Rhode Island Avenue, N.W., Washington 5, D.C.
GUIDE TO UNITED STATES GOVERNMENT PAINT

SPECIFICATIONS. Compilation of abstracts of essential data from paint specifications issued by various government agencies, the Association of State Highway Officials, and the American Society for Testing and Materials. The latest edition is the 16th, 1961, with supplements.
SUMMIT CONFERENCE ON UNIFORM LABELING. Report of a 1964 National Conference on Uniform Labeling for the purposes of laying the foundation for uniformity of labeling. Proceedings topics include hazardous substances labeling; formula labeling; flammable labeling; weights and measures labeling.

National Printing Ink Research Institute, Lehigh University, Bethlehem, Pennsylvania.
NPIRI STANDARD TEST METHODS.

National Ready Mixed Concrete Association, National Sand and Gravel Association, 1411 K Street, N.W. Washington 5, D.C.
Standards on operation of truck mixers and agitators, methods of testing mixer efficiency, and guides for concrete plants and equipment

National Sanitation Foundation, School of Public Health, University of Michigan, Ann Arbor, Michigan.
Standards on soda fountain and luncheonette equipment; spray-type dishwashing machines; commercial cooking and warming equipment; commercial hot water generating equipment; dispensing freezers; commercial refrigerators and freezers; commercial powdered food preparation equipment; food vending machine; special equipment and devices; diatomite type filters for swimming pools.
Mahoney, Tom. NATIONAL SANITATION FOUNDATION: HOW ITS STANDARDS SKIRT REFRIGERATION INDUSTRY. Air Conditioning, Heating and Refrigeration News 102:24, August 10; 28-29, August 17, 1964.

National Slag Association, 613 Perpetual Building, Washington 4, D.C.
RECOMMENDED SPECIFICATIONS FOR STRUCTURAL CONCRETE.

National Soybean Processors Association, 3818 Board of Trade Building, Chicago 4, Illinois.
YEAR BOOK contains:
Tentative Soybean Lecithin Specifications.
Standard Specifications for Crude Soybean Oil for Technical Uses.
Specifications for Crude Degummed Solvent Extracted Soybean Oil.

Standard Specifications for Refined Soybean Oil (Not Deodorized).

National Standards Association, 1315 Fourteenth Street, N.W., Washington 5, D.C.

Distributes National Aerospace Standards established by the National Aerospace Standards Committee as well as Air Force-Navy Aeronautical Standards, Air Force-Navy Aeronautical Design Standards, Military Standards issued by the Air Force and Bureau of Weapons and Military Standards issued by other branches of the armed services and used by the Air Force and the Bureau of Weapons. Indexes to the above categories of standards are also available from the Association. It also maintains photostats of specifications in its master file.
STANDARD GYRO TERMINOLOGY.
SUGGESTED SOURCES OF SUPPLY FOR NATIONAL AEROSPACE STANDARD PARTS.

National Swimming Pool Institute, 39 South LaSalle Street, Chicago 3, Illinois.

MINIMUM STANDARDS FOR PUBLIC AND SEMI-PUBLIC POOLS.
MINIMUM REQUIREMENTS FOR CONSTRUCTION AND INSTALLATION OF FIBER GLASS POOLS.
MINIMUM STANDARDS FOR RESIDENTIAL POOLS.

National Terrazzo and Mosaic Association, 711 Fourteenth Street, N.W., Washington 5, D.C.

TECHNICAL DATA AND STANDARD SPECIFICATIONS FOR TERRAZZO AND MOSAIC WORK.
SPECIFICATIONS FOR MONOLITHIC TERRAZZO.

National Water Well Association, 811 North Lincoln Avenue, Urbana, Illinois.

NWWA STANDARD CONTRACT DOCUMENTS which are collectively known as "a set of specifications for a water well." Co-developer with American Water Works Association of AWWA A100-58, AWWA STANDARD FOR DEEP WELLS, and published by the latter.

National Wooden Pallet Manufacturers Association, 1619 Massachusetts Avenue, N.W., Washington 6, D.C.

SPECIFICATIONS AND GRADES FOR HARDWOOD WAREHOUSE PALLETS.
SPECIFICATIONS FOR DOUGLAS FIR & WESTERN SOFTWOOD PLYWOOD PALLETS.

National Woodwork Manufacturers Association, 400 West Madison

Street, Chicago 6, Illinois.

MINIMUM STANDARDS FOR WATER REPELLENT PRESERVATIVE TREATMENT OF WOODWORK.

MANUAL OF FEDERAL MILLWORK SPECIFICATIONS.

The following door, window and sash Commercial Standards were initiated by the Association:

CS 120-58 Standard Stock Ponderosa Pine Doors.

CS 171-58 Hardwood Veneered Doors - Hollow Core and Solid Core.

CS 163-58 Standard Stock Ponderosa Pine Windows, Sash and Screens.

CS 190-59 Standard Stock Double-Hung Wood Window Units.

CS 193-59 Standard Stock Ponderosa Pine Insulating Glass Windows and Sash.

CS 204-59 Standard Stock Wood Awning Window and Projected Awning and Stationary Sash Units.

CS 205-59 Standard Stock Ponderosa Pine Wood Casement Units.

CS 208-57 Stock Exterior Wood Window and Door Frames. Under development are standards for single-hung wood window units, and horizontal sliding wood window units.

Natural Gas Processors Association, 429 Kennedy Building, Tulsa 3, Oklahoma.

LIQUIFIED PETROLEUM GAS SPECIFICATIONS AND TEST METHODS.

OFFICIAL SPECIFICATIONS AND METHODS OF SAMPLING AND TESTING FOR NATURAL GASOLINE.

Northern Hardwood and Pine Manufacturers Association, Suite 207, Northern Building, Green Bay, Wisconsin.

OFFICIAL GRADING RULES FOR NORTHERN WHITE PINE, NORWAY PINE, JACK PINE, EASTERN SPRUCE, NORTHERN WHITE FIR; EASTERN HEMLOCK LUMBER; NORTHERN HARDWOOD AND SOFTWOOD LOGS AND TIE CUTS.

LUMBER GRADE USE GUIDES.

Northern Pine Manufacturers' Association, 4329 Oakland Avenue, Minneapolis 7, Minnesota.

STANDARD GRADING RULES.

Outboard Industries Association, 307 North Michigan Avenue, Chicago 1, Illinois.

1964 OIA ENGINEERING MANUAL OF RECOMMENDED PRACTICES.

In addition to recommended practices for boats, motors and equipment, and trailers, it includes specifications

for boat horsepower capacity, boat weight capacity, boat flotation, pontoon boat capacity, navigation lights, fuel tanks, oil test procedures, motor horsepower, and fire standards.
The OIA includes the Outboard Boating Club of America, the Outboard Motor Manufacturers Association, the Outboard Boat Manufacturers Association, and the Boat Trailer Manufacturers Association.

Packaging Institute, 342 Madison Avenue, New York 17, New York.
CURRENT PUBLICATION LIST includes test procedures, practices, and specifications. Test Procedures include those for adhesives, films and foils, food, paper, printing, and shipping containers.

Painting and Decorating Contractors of America, 2625 West Peterson Avenue, Chicago 45, Illinois.
RECOMMENDED GUIDE TO PAINTING SPECIFICATIONS.

Perlite Institute, 45 West 45th Street, New York 36, New York.
Specifications covering the following uses of perlite: perlite gypsum plaster; perlite insulating concrete; perlite concrete in floors; silicone treated perlite loose full insulation; expanded perlite insulation for low temperatures in atmospheric service; Perl-Lome horticultural perlite.

Photographic Society of America, 2005 Walnut Street, Philadelphia 3, Pennsylvania.
UNIFORM PRACTICES:
Standard Light Source for Judging Black and White and Toned Prints.
Uniform Practice for Judging Amateur Slides and Motion Pictures.

Pipe Fabrication Institute, 992 Perry Highway, Pittsburgh, Pennsylvania.
STANDARDS include:
END PREPARATION AND MACHINED BACKING RINGS FOR BUTT WELDS; METHOD OF DIMENSIONING WELDED ASSEMBLIES; LINEAR TOLERANCES, BENDING RADII, MINIMUM TANGENTS; SHOP HYDROSTATIC TESTING OF FABRICATED PIPING; CLEANING FABRICATED PIPING; MINIMUM LENGTH AND SPACING FOR WELDED NOZZLES; RECOMMENDED PRE-HEAT AND POSTHEAT WELDING PRACTICES FOR LOW CHROMIUM-MOLYBDENUM STEEP PIPE; RECOMMENDED PRACTICE FOR SHIELDED METAL-ARC WELDING DISSIMILAR FERRITIC STEELS; RECOMMENDED PRACTICE FOR STRESS RELIEVING WELDED ATTACHMENTS; PERMANENT IDENTIFICATION

OF PIPING MATERIALS; RECOMMENDED PREHEAT AND POSTHEAT WELDING PRACTICES FOR MEDIUM CHROMIUM-MOLYBDENUM STEEL PIPE; CLASSIFICATION OF SHOP TESTING, INSPECTION, AND CLEANING; RECOMMENDED PRACTICE FOR MAGNETIC PARTICLE INSPECTION; RECOMMENDED RADIOGRAPHIC INTERPRETATION OF TUNGSTEN INERT GAS WELDS; ACCESS HOLES AND PLUGS FOR RADIOGRAPHIC INSPECTION OF PIPE WELDS; LIQUID PENETRANT INSPECTION; ULTRASONIC INSPECTION OF SEAMLESS PIPING.

Porcelain Enamel Institute, 1145 Nineteenth Street, N.W., Washington 6, D.C.

GENERAL SPECIFICATIONS FOR PORCELAIN ENAMEL SURFACES.
SPECIFICATIONS, TABLE TOPS.
PORCELAIN ENAMEL (GLASS LINED) TANKS FOR DOMESTIC HOT WATER SERVICE.
PERFORMANCE SPECIFICATION FOR PORCELAIN ENAMEL CHALK-BOARDS.
SPECIFICATION FOR ARCHITECTURAL PORCELAIN ENAMEL ON STEEL FOR EXTERIOR USE.
TENTATIVE SPECIFICATION FOR PORCELAIN ENAMEL ON ALUMINUM FOR SIGN AND ARCHITECTURAL APPLICATIONS.
RECOMMENDED STANDARD DETAILS FOR ARCHITECTURAL PROCELAIN ENAMEL FOR SERVICE STATIONS AND SIMILAR BUILDINGS.
INTERIM RECOMMENDED SPECIFICATIONS FOR VINYL AND NEOPRENE GASKETS (AS USED IN CONJUNCTION WITH ARCHITECTURAL PORCELAIN ENAMEL).

Powder Actuated Tool Manufacturers' Institute, 200 College Street, New Haven 10, Connecticut.

UNIFORM STATE CODE RELATING TO POWDER ACTUATED FASTENING TOOLS USING STUDS, PINS AND FASTENERS.

Power Saw Manufacturers Association, 2217 Tribune Tower, Chicago 11, Illinois.

TECHNICAL MANUAL OF RECOMMENDED PRACTICES. Includes standards on guide bar capacity, plunge bow capacity, all-purpose bow capacity, and basic rules for chain saw safety.

Precision Potentiometer Manufacturers' Association, 3525 Peterson Road, Chicago 45, Illinois.

INDUSTRY STANDARD FOR PRECISION POTENTIOMETER

TERMS AND DEFINITIONS.
Wrigley, A. POTENTIOMETER GROUP ISSUES STANDARD ON TEST PROCEDURES. Electronic News, September 14, 1964, p.41
Announcement of a new standard for inspection and test procedures for wirewound precision potentiometers.

Pressure Sensitive Tape Council, 1201 Waukegan Road, Glenview, Illinois.
TEST METHODS FOR PRESSURE SENSITIVE TAPES.

Prestressed Concrete Institute, 205 West Wacker Drive, Chicago 6, Illinois.
PRESTRESSED CONCRETE BUILDING CODE REQUIREMENTS.

Pulverized Limestone Association, Office of the Secretary, Sylacauga Calcium Products Company, Sylacauga, Alabama.
STANDARDIZED TEST METHODS:
Sieve analysis of "325 mesh" pulverized limestone.
Determination of the pH of calcium carbonate.
Particle size of calcium carbonate by sedimentation.
Determination of calcium oxide.

Radio Technical Commission for Aeronautics, Room 1072, Building T-5, 16th & Constitution Avenue, N.W., Washington 25, D.C.
AIRCRAFT ELECTRONIC EQUIPMENT MINIMUM PERFORMANCE STANDARDS--THEIR PURPOSE AND APPLICATION.
"A clarification of the purpose and recommended application of aircraft electronic equipment Minimum Performance Standards, outlining a philosophy for the establishment of equitable Minimum Performance Standards."

LISTING OF AVAILABLE RTCA PAPERS includes Minimum Performance Standards for airborne receiving and transmitting equipment; distance measuring equipment; radar ground speed and/or drift angle measurement; automatic dead reckoning computer; weather and ground mapping radar; emergency communications equipment; selective calling equipment; transponder equipment; altimeter equipment; direction finding equipment; and aircraft audio and interphone amplifiers, headsets, speakers, and microphones.

Rail Steel Bar Association, 38 South Dearborn Street, Chicago 3, Illinois.
RECOMMENDED PRACTICE - PUNCHING AND SHEARING.
RECOMMENDED PRACTICE - ARC WELDING.

RAIL STEEL REFERENCE BOOK.
RAIL STEEL PRODUCTS MANUAL.

Record Industry Association of America, One East 57th Street, New York 22, New York.
STANDARDS FOR STEREOPHONIC DISC RECORDS.
DIMENSIONAL STANDARDS - DISC PHONOGRAPH RECORDS FOR HOME USE.
STANDARD RECORDING AND REPRODUCING CHARACTERISTICS.

Red Cedar Shingle Bureau, 5510 White Building, Seattle 1, Washington.
GRADING RULE SPECIFICATIONS.
CERTIGRADE HANDBOOK OF RED CEDAR SHINGLES.

Resistance Welders Manufacturers' Association, 1900 Arch Street, Philadelphia 3, Pennsylvania.
BULLETIN NO. 16 - RESISTANCE WELDING EQUIPMENT STANDARDS.
RESISTANCE WELDING MANUAL, 2 volumes.
Volume 2 includes appendices with RWMA Standards; RWAA Standards; JIC Standards; and NEMA Standards.

RLM Standards Institute, Box 754, Meriden, Connecticut.
STANDARD SPECIFICATIONS FOR INDUSTRIAL LUMINAIRES.
STANDARD SPECIFICATIONS FOR INDUSTRIAL LIGHTING EQUIPMENT.

Rubber & Plastic Adhesive & Sealant Manufacturers Council, 159 North Dearborn Street, Chicago 1, Illinois.
SPECIFICATION FOR ADHESIVE-NAIL-ON APPLICATION OF GYPSUM WALLBOARD.
SPECIFICATION FOR POLYSULFIDE-BASE SEALING COMPOUNDS FOR THE BUILDING TRADE.
Also (reprinted from Flooring Magazine, June 1962) specifications for adhesives for the installation of ceramic tile.

Rubber Manufacturers Association, 444 Madison Avenue, New York 22, New York.
RECOMMENDED MINIMUM STANDARDS FOR NEW PASSENGER CAR TIRES.
HANDBOOK-SPECIFICATIONS AND TOLERANCES--RUBBER-COVERED ROLLS.
ENGINEERING STANDARD--SPECIFICATION FOR DRIVES USING NARROW V-BELTS.
STANDARDS FOR LIGHT DUTY OR FRACTIONAL HORSEPOWER V-BELTS.

STANDARD FOR STATIC CONDUCTIVE V-BELTS.
SPECIFICATION FOR RUBBER WELDING HOSE.
RUBBER HANDBOOK--SPECIFICATIONS FOR RUBBER PRODUCTS, MOLDED, EXTRUDED, LATHE-CUT, OPEN AND CLOSED CELL SPONGE.
SPECIFICATIONS FOR VINYL FLOORING; RUBBER FLOORING; FLEXIBLE VINYL COVER BASE; RUBBER COVER BASE; APPROVED CLEANERS AND POLISHES.
STANDARD PROCEDURE FOR CONDUCTING ABRASION TESTS ON THE BUREAU OF STANDARDS ABRASION MACHINE.
STANDARD CEMENT TEST METHOD FOR ELASTOMER HEELS AND SOLES; AND DEAD LOAD TEST FOR HEAT-ACTIVATED SOLE-ATTACHING CEMENTS.

Rubber Reclaimers Association, 101 West 31st Street, New York 1, New York.
SPECIFICATIONS FOR SCRAP RUBBER.

Scientific Apparatus Makers Association, 20 North Wacker Drive, Chicago 6, Illinois.
Standards on mechanical and electric chart drive speeds of circular charts; bimetallic, resistance, filled-system, and liquid-in-glass thermometers; pyrometers; temperature-emf relation for iron-constantan thermocouples; locks and keys for instrument cases; mechanical chart drives; pane cut-out dimensions; accuracy and sensitivity terminology as applied to industrial instruments; bushing and wells for temperature sensing elements; markings for adjustment means in automatic controllers; standard load cell terminology and definitions; wood laboratory equipment.

Sheet Metal and Air Conditioning Contractors' National Association, 107 Center Street, Elgin, Illinois.
SPECIFICATIONS FOR ARCHITECTURAL SHEET METAL WORK.
RECOMMENDED WARM AIR HEATING CODE.
SUMMARY OF SHEET METAL ITEMS TO BE INCLUDED IN SHEET METAL SPECIFICATIONS.
STANDARD PRACTICES IN SHEET METAL WORK:
Manual No. 1 Gutters, Conductors and Conductor Heads.
Manual No. 2 Flashings.
Manual No. 3 Skylights and Ventilators.
NATIONAL WARM AIR HEATING CODE.

Slide Fasteners Association, 366 Madison Avenue, New York 17, New York.
DEFINITIONS AND TEST METHODS FOR ZIPPERS.

Society of Aeronautical Weight Engineers, 8428 Lurline Avenue, Canoga Park, California.

WEIGHT HANDBOOK.

PUBLICATIONS AND TECHNICAL PAPERS INDEX.

Technical papers include:

Weight control in specification writing.

Specification for the standard presentation of basic data needed by an airline for purposes of weights and balances evaluation.

Standard form for weight and balance data presentation.

Secondary force standards for calibrating weighing equipment.

Derivation and dissemination of mass standards.

Evaluation of economics of passenger comfort standards.

Definition of an equipment list and standard form for weight and balance data.

Society of Automotive Engineers, 485 Lexington Avenue, New York 17, New York.

SAE HANDBOOK (Annual).

A compilation of more than 500 SAE standards, recommended practices and information reports on ferrous and non-ferrous metals; nonmetallic materials; threads, fasteners, and common parts; electrical equipment and lighting for motor vehicles and farm equipment; power plant components and accessories; passenger cars, trucks, and buses; tractor and earthmoving equipment; and marine equipment.

AMS INDEX.

Lists over 1000 SAE Aerospace Material Specifications on tolerances; quality control and process; nonmetallics; aluminum, magnesium, copper, titanium, and miscellaneous nonferrous alloys; wrought carbon steels; special purpose ferrous alloys; wrought low alloy steels; corrosion and heat resistant steels and alloys; cast iron and low alloy steels; accessories, fabricated parts and assemblies; special property materials; refractory and reactive materials.

AS, ARP, AIR INDEX.

A list of 330 SAE Aerospace Standards, Aerospace Recommended Practices, and Aerospace Information Reports. Aerospace Standards are design and part standards applicable to missile, airframe, and ground support equipment; propulsion, propeller and accessory equipment; and airline industries. Aerospace Recommended Practices give dimensional, design and performance recommendations intended as guides for standard engineering practice. Aerospace Information Reports contain engineering data and general information useful to aerospace industries.

SAE AEROSPACE-AUTOMOTIVE DRAWING STANDARDS

MANUAL presents techniques used in specifying engineering requirements on drawings used in the manufacture of aerospace and ground vehicle products. Special Publication SP 247, DIMENSIONING AND TOLERANCING STANDARDS is a reprint of several sections of this manual.

Other Society publications relating to standards, specifications and other matters are listed in SAE PUBLICATIONS, a checklist which is revised three times a year.

NEW AMDs ARE JET-FAST SPECIFICATION. AEROSPACE MATERIALS DOCUMENTS WILL GET NEW MATERIALS AND PROCESSES DATA INTO ENGINEERS HAND MONTHS FASTER. SAE Journal 70:83, October, 1962.

SAE ENGINE TECHNICAL COMMITTEE INAUGURATES FOUR NEW STANDARDIZATION PROJECTS. SAE Journal 71:125-127, May 1963.

CONSTRUCTION AND INDUSTRIAL MACHINERY TECHNICAL COMMITTEE EXPANDS STANDARDIZATION EFFORTS. SAE Journal 71:80-82, September, 1963.

Society of Motion Picture and Television Engineers, 55 West 42nd Street, New York 36, New York.

INDEX TO SMPTE-SPONSORED AMERICAN STANDARDS AND RECOMMENDED PRACTICES.

A list of some 150 Standards and Recommended Practices on apertures for cameras, printers, and projectors; film dimensions and usage; sound; television; test films; video magnetic tape recording; lamps; lens and lens mounts; reel spindles; reels; screens; splices; spools; and sprockets.

Practically every issue of the JOURNAL OF THE SMPTE has the text of new or proposed Standards and Recommended Practices.

16MM, 35MM TEST FILMS.

A descriptive catalog of test films planned by technical committees of the Society.

Alden, A. E. SMPTE AND THE AMERICAN STANDARDS PROGRAM. Journal of the SMPTE 71:850-853, November 1962.

Matthews, G. E. A NOTE ON THE EARLY HISTORY OF THE SOCIETY AND ITS WORK ON STANDARDIZATION. Journal of the SMPTE 72:196-202, March 1963.

Society of Naval Architects and Marine Engineers, 74 Trinity Place, New York 6, New York.

PUBLICATIONS OF THE TECHNICAL AND RESEARCH COMMITTEES.

The following standards publications are listed:

UNIFORM PROCEDURE FOR THE CALCULATION OF FRICTIONAL RESISTANCE AND THE EXPANSION OF

MODEL TEST DATA TO FULL SIZE; TENTATIVE CODE FOR THE SELECTION OF WROUGHT ALUMINUM ALLOYS FOR SHIP STRUCTURES; TENTATIVE STANDARD ALUMINUM ALLOY TEE AND ANGLE SHAPES FOR SHIP STRUCTURES; RECOMMENDED PRACTICES FOR PREPARING MARINE POWER PLANT HEAT BALANCES STANDARD LIFEBOAT CODE; STANDARDIZATION TRIALS CODE; ECONOMY AND ENDURANCE TRIALS CODE; CODE ON MANEUVERING AND SPECIAL TRIALS AND TESTS; CODE ON INSTRUMENTS AND APPARATUS FOR SHIP TRIALS; CODE ON INSTALLATION AND SHOP TESTS.

Society of Plastics Engineers, 65 Prospect Street, Stamford, Connecticut.

STANDARD PROPERTY LIST FOR PLASTICS MATERIALS.

Society of the Plastics Industry, 250 Park Avenue, New York 17, New York.

STANDARDS ON PLASTICS PRODUCTS.
A list of the Commercial Standards promulgated by the U.S. Department of Commerce in cooperation with the Society.
TENTATIVE URETHANE FOAM BUYER'S SPECIFICATION FOR BEDDING AND SEAT CUSHIONING.
SUGGESTIONS FOR INCLUSION OF PLASTIC PIPE AND FITTINGS IN GOVERNMENTAL, STATE, MUNICIPAL AND OTHER REGULATORY BODY PLUMBING CODES.
METHOD OF TEST FOR RATE OF RISE PROPERTIES OF URETHANE FOAM.
PRESS RELEASE: JERRY CAN STANDARDS BEING DEVELOPED BY THE PLASTICS INDUSTRY.

Southern Building Code Congress, Brown-Marx Building, Birmingham 3, Alabama.

SOUTHERN STANDARDS BUILDING CODE.
SOUTHERN GAS CODE, PART II.
SOUTHERN PLUMBING CODE, PART III.
SOUTHERN HOUSING CODE, PART IV.
APPROVAL REPORTS on materials, products, or assemblies and their compliance with the codes.

Southern Pine Inspection Bureau, 520 National Bank of Commerce Building, New Orleans 4, Louisiana.

SPIB STANDARDS FOR SOUTHERN PINE ROOF DECKING (DOUBLE TONGUE AND GROOVE).
STANDARD GRADING RULES FOR SOUTHERN PINE LUMBER.
FHA GRADE MARKING AND THE SPIB.

STANDARD SPECIFICATIONS FOR GLUED LAMINATED SOUTHERN PINE.

Specialty Paper and Board Affiliates, 122 East 42nd Street, New York 17, New York.

STANDARDS FOR POLYETHYLENE EXTRUSION COATING.
STANDARD TEST PROCEDURE FOR WATER VAPOR TRANSMISSION RATE.
STANDARD TEST METHOD FOR SLIP DETERMINATION.

Standards Engineers Society, 170 Livingston Avenue, Providence, New Jersey.

PROCEEDINGS OF Annual Meetings.
STANDARDS ENGINEERING, monthly magazine.

Steatite Manufacturers Association, 53 Park Place, New York, New York.

STANDARDS OF THE STEATITE MANUFACTURERS ASSOCIATION.
A compilation of manufacturing standards; general test methods; military specification qualification samples; inspection by acceptance sampling; test specimens; loss factor tests; dielectric strength tests; flexural strength tests; resistance to thermal change test; nonporosity (Fuchsine Dye) test; and definitions.

Steel Founders' Society of America, 606 Terminal Tower, Cleveland 13, Ohio.

RECOMMENDED MINIMUM STANDARD FOR COMMERCIAL CARBON STEEL CASTINGS.
RAW MATERIAL SPECIFICATIONS on Gelatinized Cereal Binder; Zicron Sand and Flour; Washed and Dried Sand; Western Bentonite; Crude Sand; Fosterite and/or Olivine; Cast Steel Abrasives; and Malleable Iron Abrasives.

Steel Door Institute, 2130 Keith Building, Cleveland 13, Ohio.

PROPOSED AMERICAN STANDARD NOMENCLATURE FOR STEEL DOORS AND STEEL DOOR FRAMES.
COMMERCIAL STANDARD CS211-57 - FLUSH-TYPE INTERIOR STEEL DOORS AND FRAMES.
COMMERCIAL STANDARD CS242-62 - STANDARD STOCK COMMERCIAL 13/4 - INCH THICK STEEL DOORS AND FRAMES.

Steel Joist Institute, 1346 Connecticut Avenue, N.W., Washington 6, D.C.

STANDARD SPECIFICATIONS AND LOAD TABLES - OPEN WEB STEEL JOISTS.

RECOMMENDED CODE OF STANDARD PRACTICE.

Steel Shipping Container Institute, 600 Fifth Avenue, New York 20, New York.

SPECIFICATION FOR 55 GALLON (U.S.) TIGHT HEAD UNIVERSAL DRUM.

RECOMMENDED SPECIFICATION FOR PALLETIZING 5-GALLON, STRAIGHT-SIDE AND NESTING PAILS.

MH2.1-1959 THROUGH MH2.10-1959. AMERICAN STANDARD SPECIFICATION FOR METAL DRUMS AND PAILS.

MH2.2.11-1960 THROUGH MH2.14-1960. AMERICAN STANDARD SPECIFICATION FOR METAL DRUMS.

Steel Structures Painting Council, 4440 Fifth Avenue, Pittsburch 13, Pennsylvania.

STEEL STRUCTURE PAINTING MANUAL.

Volume 2 is on "Systems and Specifications," a complete painting guide and index of recommended painting systems for most steel structures in various exposures.

SURFACE PREPARATION SPECIFICATIONS.

Deal with solvent cleaning, hand cleaning, power tool cleaning, flame cleaning of new steel, blast cleaning to "white metal," commercial blast cleaning, brush-off blast cleaning, pickling, weathering and pickling.

PRETREAT SPECIFICATIONS.

Include cover wetting oil treatment, cold phosphate surface treatment, basic zinc chromate-vinyl butyral washcoat, and hot phosphate surface treatment.

PAINT APPLICATION SPECIFICATIONS deal with shop, field, and maintenance painting.

Also 20 PAINT AND PAINT SYSTEM SPECIFICATIONS.

Steel Window Institute, 18455 Harvest Lane, Brookfield, Wisconsin.

RECOMMENDED STANDARDS FOR STEEL WINDOWS.

Structural Clay Products Institute, 1520 18th Street, N.W., Washington 6, D.C.

SCPI RECOMMENDED SPECIFICATIONS FOR CLAY MASONRY CONSTRUCTION.

ASTM SPECIFICATIONS FOR CLAY MASONRY UNITS AND MORTAR.

Technical Association of the Pulp and Paper Industry, 360 Lexington Avenue, New York 17, New York.

TAPPI STANDARDS, a looseleaf manual of official, tentative, and suggested methods.

YEARBOOK includes "Regulations Governing Standards

and Suggested Methods," and an "Index of Standards and Suggested Methods." More than 800 are indexed covering virtually all aspects of pulp and paper testing.
BIBLIOGRAPHY OF PAPERMAKING, annual. Contains a section on Specifications in which books, journal articles, and standards and specifications are listed.
Field, J.W. TAPPI UNIFIES PAPER INDUSTRY GOALS AND METHODS. Analytical Chemistry 31:21A-30A, August 1959.

3-A Sanitary Standards Committees, Room 512, 1145 19th Street, N.W., Washington 6, D.C.
ORGANIZATION OF 3A SANITARY STANDARDS FOR DAIRY EQUIPMENT.
Brochure describing the set-up of the organization and its various task committees.
HOLDERS OF AUTHORIZATIONS TO USE THE 3-A SYMBOL ... In addition to listing the names of companies whose practices conform to 3-A Sanitary Standards, it also lists the more than 30 standards dealing with storage, processing and transporation equipment used by the industry.
The standards and amendments to them are issued as reprints from the Journal of Milk and Food Technology in which they are originally published. Reports of the work of the Committee also appears in the latter journal.
The most-recently promulgated standard, to be effective after January 20, 1965 is PACKAGING EQUIPMENT FOR FROZEN DESSERTS, COTTAGE CHEESE, AND SIMILAR MILK PRODUCTS.
QUESTIONS AND ANSWERS ABOUT 3-A SANITARY STANDARDS FOR DAIRY EQUIPMENT Journal of Milk and Food Technology 19:260-264, September 1956.

Tile Council of America, 800 Second Avenue, New York 17, New York.
STANDARD SPECIFICATIONS FOR INSTALLATION OF CERAMIC TILE WITH WATER RESISTANT ORGANIC ADHESIVES.
AMERICAN STANDARD SPECIFICATIONS FOR INSTALLATION OF CERAMIC TILE WITH DRY-SET PORTLAND CEMENT MORTAR.
AMERICAN STANDARD SPECIFICATIONS FOR GLAZED CERAMIC WALL TILE, CERAMIC MOSAIC TILE, QUARRY TILE AND PAVERS INSTALLED IN PORTLAND CEMENT MORTARS.

Tire and Rim Association, Command Building, 34 North Hawkins Avenue, Akron 13, Ohio.
YEARBOOK.
Annually revised standards dealing with maximum tire

loads at various inflation pressures, and dimensions of rims and rim contours, and vlave and valve hole dimensions. The tires, rims, valves and tubes are those used in passenger cars, motorcycles and motor scooters, trucks and buses, trailers, vehicles for earthmoving, mining and logging, road graders, mobile cranes, shovels, mining cars and cutters, agricultural tractors and implements, industrial vehicles, mobile homes, and aircraft.

Toilet Goods Association, 1270 Avenue of the Americas, New York 20, New York.

SPECIFICATIONS on raw materials for use in cosmetics, such as, glycerin, boric acid, petrolatum, petroleum wax, beeswax, talc, precipitated chalk, titanium dioxide, and about 100 additional products.

Trailer Coach Association, 1340 West Third Street, Los Angeles 17, California.

PROPOSED TRAVEL TRAILER STANDARDS FOR PLUMBING, HEATING AND ELECTRICAL SYSTEMS.

PROPOSED MOBILE HOME STANDARDS FOR PLUMBING, HEATING AND ELECTRICAL SYSTEMS.

Tubular and Split Rivet Council, 53 Park Place, New York 7, New York.

DIMENSIONAL STANDARDS FOR SEMI-TUBULAR RIVETS, FULL TUBULAR RIVETS, SPLIT RIVETS AND RIVET CAPS.

STANDARDS OF TUBULAR EXCHANGER MANUFACTURERS ASSOCIATION.

A compilation of standards on nomenclature; fabrication tolerances; general fabrication and performance; installation, operation and maintenance; mechanical standards TEMA Class R heat exchangers; mechanical standards TEMA Class C heat exchangers; material specifications; thermal standards; physical properties of fluids; general design data.

Rubin, F. L. WHAT ARE THE DIFFERENCES? NEW TEMA STANDARDS COMPARED TO OLD. Hydrocarbon Process & Petroleum Refiner 40:157-164, June 1961.

Underwriters' Laboratories, 207 East Ohio Street, Chicago 11, Illinois.

STANDARDS FOR SAFETY.

This list of published standards includes over 200 that provide specifications and requirements for construction and performance under test and in actual use of a broad range of electrical apparatus and equipment, including household appliances; fire extinguishing and fire protection devices and equipment; and many other non-generally classifiable items such as ladders, sweeping compounds, waste cans, and roof jacks for trailer coaches.

Oliver, F. J. APPROVAL OF UNDERWRITERS' LABORATORIES STANDARDS AS AMERICAN STANDARDS. Electrical Manufacturing 63:156-160, April 1959.

Horn, L. TESTING FOR PUBLIC SAFETY. Institute of Electrical and Electronics Engineers-Transactions on Broadcast & Television Receivers vol. BTR-9:104-107, July 1963.

Review of the organization, purpose and methods of UL as applied to testing and listing radio and television receivers.

United States Pharmacopeial Convention, 46 Park Avenue, New York 16, New York.

UNITED STATES PHARMACOPEIA.

Current edition contains over 900 monographs on drugs and dosage forms.

LIST OF REFERENCE STANDARDS. Highly purified specimens of drugs intended for use in testing commercial preparations.

Upholstery Leather Group, 411 Fifth Avenue, New York, New York.

UPHOLSTERY LEATHER; INDUSTRY SPECIFICATIONS AND STANDARDS.

Vermiculite Institute, 208 South LaSalle Street, Chicago 4, Illinois.

STANDARD SPECIFICATIONS FOR VERMICULITE PLASTERING AND ACOUSTICAL PLASTIC FOR SOUND-CONDITIONING.

VERMICULITE TYPE-MK-3 FIREPROOFING--SPECIFICATIONS AND TECHNICAL DATA.

SPECIFICATIONS FOR VERMICULITE INSULATING CONCRETE--ROOF INSULATION AND ROOF DECKS.

VERMICULITE FIRE-RESISTANCE RATINGS--PLASTER, ACOUSTICAL PLASTER, TYPE-MK, CONCRETE.

Water Conditioning Foundation, 1201 Waukegan Road, Glenview, Illinois.

RECOMMENDED INDUSTRY STANDARDS FOR HOUSEHOLD WATER SOFTENERS.

RECOMMENDED INSTALLATION PROCEDURES FOR HOUSEHOLD WATER CONDITIONING EQUIPMENT.

Welded Steel Tube Institute, 1604 Hanna Building, Cleveland 15, Ohio.

HANDBOOK OF WELDED STEEL TUBING contains a

listing and brief description of 50 specifications and standards issued by various trade associations, technical societies, and the Federal government on welded tubing and the Federal government on welded tubing and piping.

Western Pine Association, Yeon Building, Portland 4, Oregon.
STANDARD GRADING RULES FOR LUMBER of certain species of pine, fir, larch, spruce, cedar, and hemlock.
STRUCTURAL GLUED LAMINATED LARCH--STANDARD SPECIFICATION FOR DESIGN AND FABRICATION.
LUMBER TECHNICAL MANUAL includes a description of lumber grades and lumber specifications data.

West Coast Lumberman's Association, 1410 S.W. Morrison Street, Portland 5, Oregon.
STANDARD GRADING AND DRESSING RULES for Douglas Fir, West Coast hemlock, sitka spruce and Western red cedar.
STANDARD SPECIFICATIONS FOR STRUCTURAL GLUED LAMINATED DOUGLAS FIR (COAST REGION) TIMBER.
WEST COAST LUMBER GRADES, USES, SPECIFICATIONS.
SPECIFICATION AND DESIGN RECOMMENDATIONS FOR WEST COAST DOUGLAS FIR in bridges, docks, warehouses and other structures.
SPECIFICATIONS FOR: LAMINATED BLOCK FLOORING OF 3 PLY OR 5 PLY CONSTRUCTION SET IN MASTIC; HERRINGBONE FLOORING SET IN MASTIC: MASTIC CUSHIONED CONSTRUCTION WITH NAILERS, SUBFLOORING AND FINISH FLOORING; MASTIC-NAILED CONSTRUCTION WITH MASTIC-SET SUB-FLOORING AND NAILED FINISH FLOORING: STEEL-SPLINED CONTINUOUS STRIP MASTIC-SET MAPLE FLOORING; RUBBER CUSHION-SLEEPER CONSTRUCTION WITH NAILERS AND FINISH FLOORING.
RECOMMENDATIONS FOR THE CORRECT PREPARATION, FINISHING AND TESTING OF CONCRETE SUBFLOOR SURFACES TO RECEIVE WOOD FLOORING.

Woven Fabric Belting Manufacturers Association, 27 William Street, New York 5, New York.
SOLID WOVEN COTTON BELTING.
Includes recommended standards.

Yacht Safety Bureau, 336 Old Hook Road, Westwood, New Jersey.
TENTATIVE CLASSIFICATION STANDARDS:
REQUIREMENTS FOR MARINE FUEL FILTERS, STRAINERS AND SEPARATORS.
REQUIREMENTS FOR MARINE NAVIGATION LIGHTS.
REQUIREMENTS FOR MARINE BATTERY CHARGERS.
Also issued or under development are standards for

alcohol and kerosene galley stoves; galley stoves operated with solid fuels; metal fuel tanks; marine rectifiers; battery switches; fuel tanks made of fiberglass reinforced plastics; flame arrester assemblies for carburetors; tube fittings; fuel valves; flexible fuel line sections; electrical pumps; and combustible gas indicators.

Automotive Air Conditioning Association, 6300 North Central Expressway, Dallas 6, Texas.

ACCA-STANDARD 100-64 FOR VEHICLE AIR CONDITIONERS AIR QUANTITY CERTIFICATION.

NOTE: No effort has been made in the foregoing list of organizations to indicate which among the thousands of standards they issue have achieved the designation "American Standard." Attention is called to the American Standard Association's annual CATALOG OF AMERICAN STANDARDS which contains an "Organizational Cross Index." It is a cross index to those American Standards that carry the designations of other organizations. The current (1965) CATALOG OF AMERICAN STANDARDS lists 38 organizations and about 1500 American Standards in this cross index.

Section 6

INTERNATIONAL STANDARDIZATION

Section 6

INTERNATIONAL STANDARDIZATION

The American Standards Association is the clearing house for information on international standardization activities and the sales agent in the United States for standards documents issued by international standards bodies and the national standardizing agencies in foreign countries. The ASA is the U.S. Member-Body of the International Organization for Standardization (ISO), which has fifty national standard bodies as its world members, and also a member of the International Electrotechnical Commission (IEC). The U.S. National Committee of the IEC has administrative and technical affiliation with the ASA. The IEC, in turn, is affiliated with the ISO as a technical division. The object of the IEC is to facilitate the coordination and unification of national electrotechnical standards and to coordinate the activities of other international organizations in the field. Finally, ASA is a member of the Pan American Standards Committee created several years ago to foster inter-American standardization. ASA NEWSLETTER of September 1964 reported the approval of the first set of Pan American Standards: "Acting to abolish century-old non-tariff trade barriers and thereby present a common market of Latin America to the world, the 15-nation Pan American Standards Committee has approved the first set of 56 Pan American Standards. Thirty-two test methods for carbon steel, 17 for textiles and seven for metallurgy constitute the first continent-wide industry standards sanctioned by the PASC since its reorganization in 1961."

Available from the ASA is a booklet entitled WORLD STANDARDS - COMMON GROUND FOR BUYER AND SELLER IN WORLD TRADE, a concise description of how international standards are developed through the ISO, the IEC, and other channels and how ASA participates.

The ASA's 1964 CATALOG OF AMERICAN STANDARDS includes a listing of 300 ISO Recommendations and notes the availability of ISO MEMENTO, an annual publication containing general information on the ISO, together with a list of Member Bodies and of Administrative and Technical Committees, a table of participation by country, and a numerical and subject list of ISO and draft ISO Recommendations.

The 1964 CATALOG OF AMERICAN STANDARDS also has a list of IEC Recommendations and notes the availability of IEC CENTRAL OFFICE REPORT, an annual publication describing the technical work of the IEC. Included is a list of scheduled meetings, reports of work in progress in each technical committee and subcommittee, publications issued, and draft recommendations in process. THE ASA has prepared for April 1965 publication a booklet entitled: LIST OF INFORMATION PUBLICATIONS ON ISO AND IEC.

The ASA's MAGAZINE OF STANDARDS announces newly-available International Recommendations and lists new standards from other countries. There are frequent articles describing developments on the international standards front.

The International Commission on Rules for the Approval of Electrical Equipment (CEE) is referred to by ASA as one of the most powerful code-making organizations in the world. In general, it deals with the same kinds of products that, in the United States, are listed by Underwriters' Laboratories. CEE Specifications are used as the basis for the regulations that control approval of electrical products for sale throughout most of Europe. A list of these CEE Specifications also appears in the 1964 CATALOG OF AMERICAN STANDARDS which also notes the availability of CEE STATUTES AND RULES OF PROCEDURE (1961) which describes CEE's method of operation.

The previously-noted CATALOG OF SELECTED FOREIGN ELECTRICAL STANDARDS is distributed by the American Standards Association. It is a classified list of national electrical standards issued by 38 foreign countries.

Regional, as well as national and international standards programs are in existence. EURONORMS are standards on iron and steel products published by the High Authority of the European Coal and Steel Community. A list of 29 currently-available standards is available from ASA. INSTA (INTER-NORDIC STANDARDIZATION) are standards prepared jointly by the standardizing bodies of Denmark, Finland, Norway and Sweden. ASA states that there is only one now ready--on welded pressure vessels.

The United Nation's Economic Commission for Europe sponsors a Working Party on Standardization of Perishable Foodstuffs which has prepared European Standards for individual commodities. A 1963 UN publication, AGRI/WP.1/238, STANDARDIZATION OF FRUITS AND VEGETABLES IN EUROPE. PRINCIPLES AND PRACTICE, describes the procedures of this Working Party.

The United Nation's World Health Organization has published EUROPEAN STANDARDS FOR DRINKING WATER; INTERNATIONAL STANDARDS FOR DRINKING WATER; and SPECIFICATIONS FOR PESTICIDES, INSECTICIDES, RODENTICIDES, MULLUSCICIDES, HERBICIDES, AUXILIARY CHEMICALS, SPRAYING AND DUSTING APPARATUS.

A considerable amount of attention is being focused on the work being done by the Codex Alimentarius Commission, an undertaking co-sponsored by the World Health Organization and the Food and Agriculture Organization of the United Nations. The main task of the Commission is to integrate and accelerate the work on food standards at present being carried on throughout the world by some 150 organizations. In TENTATIVE GUIDELINES FOR THE CODEX ALIMENTARIUS COMMISSION, the FAO/WHO stated the purposes of the Codex Alimentarius were to:

1. Promote international trade in food;
2. Facilitate food standards work in developing countries;
3. Protect consumers' health;
4. Ensure fair practices in the food trade.

The JOURNAL OF COMMERCE, June 30, 1964, reported favorable progress toward international food standardization at a meeting held in Washington, D.C. by a committee of food experts from thirteen nations. The committee, formed by the Codex Alimentarius Commission, adopted a basic format for voluntary quality standards aimed at insuring the marketing of sound, wholesome products, correctly labeled and presented so that the consumer can know what he is buying.

An-up-to-date summary of the work of the Codex Alimentarius Commission is available in the following references:

Koenig, N. A NEW VITAL INFLUENCE IN INTERNATIONAL FOOD STANDARDS. Food Drug Cosmetic Law Journal 19:326-336, June 1964.

Depew, F.M. NATIONAL AND INTERNATIONAL FOOD STANDARDS. Food Drug Cosmetic Law Journal 19:491-497, September 1964.

A resume of General Food Labelling Provisions Compiled by the Legislation Research Branch of the Codex Alimentarius Commission is presented in:

GENERAL FOOD LABELLING PROVISIONS. Food Drug Cosmetic Law Journal 19:460-490, September 1964.

The information given in the article is based upon replies to a questionnaire returned by sixteen out of thirty-five countries who were queried about details of label indication of food identity, weight, measure, and quantity, provision for tracing the source of the foodstuff, and other matters.

The United Nation's wide-flung interest in standardization is exemplified as well by the following report:

IN-PLANT STANDARDIZATION IN DEVELOPING COUNTRIES. E/C.5/56 and Add.1. February 1964. 124 p.

The Organization for Economic Cooperation and Development (OECD) is also standards-oriented and has published a number of reports in its Documentation Series:

19. TRIAL SHIPMENTS FOR THE EUROPEAN STANDARDIZATION OF PEARS AND CITRUS FRUIT.

25. STANDARDIZATION OF WOODEN PACKAGING FOR FRUIT AND VEGETABLES.

43. MEAT GRADING IN O.E.E.C. MEMBER COUNTRIES.

47. INTERNATIONAL STANDARDS FOR FRUITS AND VEGETABLES.

Two special numbers of an OECD journal, the Productivity Measurement Review, have been devoted to standardization:

Easterfield, T. E. STANDARDIZATION AS AN AID TO PRODUCTIVITY. Special Number, June 1962.

Smith-Gavine, S.A.N. A PERCENTAGE MEASURE OF STANDARDIZATION. Special Number, December 1963.

The OECD has active standardization programs under consideration by representatives of the member countries, two of the current ones being:

OECD SCHEME FOR THE APPLICATION OF INTERNATIONAL STANDARDS FOR FRUITS AND VEGETABLES.

OECD SCHEME FOR STANDARDIZING THE TESTING OF AGRICULTURAL MACHINERY.

A recently-formed standardizing body is the European Committee on the Coordination of Standards (CEN) whose aim is to establish standards common to the countries of the European Economic Community and those belonging to the European Free Trade Association in order to promote commerce and interchange of services among those countries. The secretariat of this organization was assigned to AFNOR, the French standards body. However, according to BSI NEWS, September 1964, a working party of the European Free Trade Association "has underlined that there can be no question of any separate EFTA standards system and the objective of EFTA countries is to make as effective as possible the work of the existing international standards organizations . . ."

The International Office of Consumers' Unions (IOCU) was organized in 1960 to serve as a clearing house for the exchange of information among consumer testing organizations similar to Consumers Union of the U.S. Twenty-three such organizations, all members of IOCU, have been established in eighteen countries. The International Organization for Standardization (ISO) has established relations with the IOCU for the purpose of standardizing international symbols designed to inform consumers about precautions to be taken with certain textile fabrics intended for clothing and household use. In addition, the IOCU has authorized its Research Committee to start work on the formulation of standard test methods to be made available for use by its member-bodies. The first two such projects deal with standard test methods for refrigerators and vacuum cleaners. The ISO has offered assistance to the IOCU and has urged it to conduct its standards formulation work through the ISO.

Several of the more recent references from the Magazine of

Standards have been selected as sources of additional information on international standardization:

WORLD VIEWPOINTS OF STANDARDIZATION. Magazine of Standards 35:108-109, April 1964.

ISO COUNCIL ACTS; REFLECTS EXPANDING WORLD INTERESTS. Magazine of Standards 34:247-248, August 1963.

THE ISO ADVISES CONSUMER ORGANIZATIONS. Magazine of Standards 35:269-270, September 1964.

UN STUDIES NEED FOR STANDARDS IN DEVELOPING COUNTRIES. Magazine of Standards 34:273, September 1963.

McAdams, W. A. CEE: CHALLENGE OR OPPORTUNITY FOR AMERICAN INDUSTRY? Magazine of Standards 34:3-6, January 1963.

ELECTRICAL INDUSTRY BENEFITS FROM IEC PARTICIPATION. Magazine of Standards 35:265-268, September 1964.

Hoffman, S. D. IEC IN FRANCE. Magazine of Standards 35:227-232, August 1964.

IEC meetings are convened periodically in various countries. This is an account of what transpired at a recent one. The article includes the names and company or association affiliation of the 86 members of the U.S. National Committee Delegation.

Hoffman, S. D. THE U.S. NATIONAL COMMITTEE OF IEC--HOW IT WORKS IN RELATION TO NATIONAL AND INTERNATIONAL STANDARDIZATION. Magazine of Standards 34:186-187, June 1963.

HOW CEN WORKS TO COORDINATE EUROPEAN NATIONAL STANDARDS. Magazine of Standards 34:309-310, October 1963.

Binney, H.A.R. STANDARDS IN THE EUROPEAN COMMON MARKET. Magazine of Standards 33:341-342, November 1962.

Hoffman, S. D. STANDARDS, ANTITRUST, AND THE COMMON MARKET. Magazine of Standards 34:46-47, February 1963.

Townsend, J. R. TECHNICAL COMMITTEES WORK TOWARD PAN-AMERICAN STANDARDS. Magazine of Standards 34:41-42, February 1963.

Eden, J. F. LATIN AMERICA AT THE CROSSROADS; STANDARDS PLAY IMPORTANT ROLE IN DEVELOPING INDUSTRY AND TRADE. Magazine of Standards 34:305-308, October 1963.

STANDARDIZATION IN CENTRAL AMERICA. Magazine of Standards 34:7, January 1963.

A grant from the National Science Foundation enabled the Library of Congress to compile an extremely useful guide to international scientific organizations:

Library of Congress. INTERNATIONAL SCIENTIFIC ORGANIZATIONS; A GUIDE TO THEIR LIBRARY, DOCUMENTATION, AND INFORMATION SERVICES. Washington, D.C.: Government Printing Office, 1962. 794p.

Prepared under the direction of Katherine O. Murra of the International Organizations Section, Reference Department of the Library of Congress. At least 50 of the 449 organizations described in this volume participate in standardization activity. The detailed information given for each organization--organization, meetings, library facilities, publications, history--includes, where pertinent, a statement relating to standards.

Some examples follow:

Committee for European Construction Equipment, 121 Queen Victoria Street, London E.C.4, England.

"Its object is to permit interested European manufacturers of construction equipment to cooperate in the study of all questions of common interest, such as conditions for tests, terminology, standardization, and the exchange of information."

European Committee for Boilermaking and Sheet Metal Working, 15 rue Beaujen, Paris 8^{e}, France.

"Its Technical Committee maintains close liaison with the International Organization for Standardization, expecially in the work of two of ISO's Technical Committees--TC 11 (Unification of Boiler Codes), and TC 58 (gas Cylinders).

International Detergent Committee, 70, Champs-Elysees, Paris 8^{e}, France.

One of the purposes of this Committee is the preparation of international standards in the fields of terminology, analysis, and test methods.

International Seed Testing Association, Binnenhaven, 1, Wageningen, The Netherlands.

Establishes procedures for the determination of seed quality based on uniform testing methods.

A thorough perusal of INTERNATIONAL SCIENTIFIC ORGANIZATIONS has indicated that, in addition to the four agencies cited above, standards activity information is also included for the following organizations:

Convention of European Constructural Steelwork Associations.

European Atomic Energy Society.

European Committee for Concrete.

European Committee of Foundry Associations.

Intergovernmental Maritime Consultative Organization.

International Association of Microbiological Societies.

International Association of Seismology and Physics of the Earth's Interior.

International Association of Wood Anatomists.

International Atomic Energy Agency.

International Briquetting Association.

International Bureau for the Standardization of Man-Made Fibers.

International Bureau of Weights and Measures.

International Conference for Promoting Technical Uniformity on Railways.

International Congress on Combustion Engines.

International Commission on Rules for the Approval of Electrical Equipment.

International Electrotechnical Commission.

International Federation for Medical Electronics.

International Federation of Engineers of Automotive Technics.

International Federation of Library Associations.

International Institute of Refrigeration.

International Institute of Welding.

International North Pacific Fisheries Commission.

International Organization for Standardization.

International Organization of Legal Metrology.

International Scientific Film Association.

International Scientific Radio Union.

International Silk Association.

International Society of Haematology.

International Speleological Congresses.

International Telecommunication Union.

International Union of Crystallography.

International Union of Forest Research.

International Union of Nutritional Sciences.

International Union of Pure and Applied Physics.

International Union of Railways.

Organization of American States.

Pan American Association of Ophthalmology.

Pan-Pacific Surgical Association.

Technical Association of the Pulp and Paper Industry.

World Metrological Organization.

There are fifty national standardizing bodies in foreign countries, all ISO members, and all busy promulgating standards and producing publications and documents. The Canadian Standards Association, for example, issues a LIST OF PUBLICATIONS, A YEARBOOK, AND THE CSA NEWS BULLETIN. The British Standards Institution has a monthly B.S.I. NEWS and the annual BRITISH STANDARDS YEARBOOK which lists and describes several thousand British Standards.

An excellent source of information about each of these national standardizing bodies is an International Organization for Standardization publication: GENERAL INFORMATION ON THE ISO MEMBER BODIES, May 1961. ISO/INF.2. Detailed information on each standardizing body is presented under twelve headings: I. Origin; II. Creation; III. Members: Nature and Number; IV. Finances; V. Staff; VI. Organizational Structure; VII. Functioning; VIII. Methods Used for Drafting Standards; IX. Nature of Standards; X. Number of Standards Published; XI. Other Periodical Publications; XII. Marks Indicating Conformity with Standards.

Additional information on the standards work going on in individual countries may be found in the following articles:

De Ciaburri, B.G. HOW ARGENTINA DEVELOPS STANDARDS. Magazine of Standards 32:68-70, March 1961.

Sa, Paulo. THE REGIME OF WEIGHTS AND MEASURES IN BRAZIL. Magazine of Standards 35:39-40, February 1964.

Ballard, B. G. STANDARDIZATION IN CANADA. Engineering Journal 44:126-127+, October 1961.

Zeldis, L. STANDARDIZATION IN CHILE. Materials Research & Standards 2:416, May 1962.

Birle, J. STANDARDIZATION IN FRANCE. Magazine of Standards 32:106-109, April 1961.

Zinzen, A. DIN STANDARDS--THE WORK OF THE GERMAN STANDARDS ASSOCIATION. Magazine of Standards 34:363-367, December 1963.

INDIA'S INDUSTRIES STUDY STANDARDS. Magazine of Standards 34:331-333, November 1963.

Swenson, T. L. PRODUCT STANDARDS FOR IRAN; BUREAU OF STANDARDS PROJECTS, TRAINING REQUIREMENTS AND REGIONAL COORDINATION. Food Technology 13:14+, October 1959.

STANDARDIZATION IN THE REPUBLIC OF KOREA. Magazine of Standards 35:195-197, July 1964.

Del Mundo, S. STANDARDIZATION OF PHILLIPINE PRODUCTS. Phillipine Economy Review 6:9-13, November-December 1959.

Viatkine, A. Y. STANDARDIZATION IN USSR-1. Magazine of Standards 33:232-234, August 1962. Part 2. 33:268-272, September 1962.

VENEZUELA ORGANIZES FOR STANDARDS; VENEZUELAN COMMISSION FOR INDUSTRIAL STANDARDS. Magazine of Standards 30:298-299, October 1959.

The Magazine of Standards for May 1963 carries a notice of the following book:

INDUSTRIAL JAPAN. SUPERIORITY OF STANDARDIZED AND QUALITY-CONTROLLED PRODUCTS. Tokyo, Japan: Standards

Division, Agency of Industrial Science and Technology, Ministry of International Trade and Industry, 1962. 40 p.

Explains relationship between the development of Japanese industry and the use of industrial standards. Individual chapters deal with standards in building construction, civil engineering, ceramics, metals, shipbuilding, railroad equipment, mechanical engineering, automobiles, motorcycles, bicycles, and other products and fields. A special section presents the history and describes the progress of industrial standards.

The published proceedings of the annual conferences on standards sponsored by the American Standards Association frequently include papers on various aspects of international standardization and standards activities in countries abroad. These aspects of standardization are especially well-presented in the Proceedings of the Fourteenth National Conference on Standards, held in 1964. The following papers are pertinent:

INTERNATIONAL RELATIONS IN STANDARDIZATION, by T. T. Miller.

IMPORTANCE OF INCREASED AMERICAN PARTICIPATION IN INTERNATIONAL STANDARDS, by J. Cohelan.

NUCLEAR SAFETY STANDARDIZATION AT THE INTERNATIONAL LEVEL, by M. C. Leverett.

CANADIAN EXPERIENCE WITH INTERNATIONAL STANDARDS, by R. F. Leggett.

THE INTERNATIONAL ORGANIZATION FOR STANDARDIZATION, by H. St.Leger.

THE PAN AMERICAN STANDARDS COMMITTEE, by B. G. de Ciaburri.

WHY DOES INDIA PARTICIPATE IN INTERNATIONAL WORK? by L. C. Verman.

EUROPEAN VIEWPOINTS ON STANDARDIZATION, by O. Sturen.

WORLD STANDARDS FOR WORLD TRADE, by J. H. Holloman.

Section 7

PERIODICALS

Section 7

PERIODICALS

There are many hundreds of technical and trade journals in the United States whose editors keep readers informed on developments in standards and specifications The extent and frequency of such coverage varies widely. The following list represents a selection of titles based upon a compilation of over 2500 standards and specifications articles published since 1959. Most of the 2500 articles were indexed in the periodicals indexes discussed in Section II. The starred titles were the more frequently cited ones, at least 15 articles or more appearing in the six-year period. Several journals, such as the CONSTRUCTION SPECIFIER and BUILDING STANDARDS MONTHLY, although not indexed, are included because they are publications of trade associations predominantly concerned with standards, specifications, and codes. STANDARDS ENGINEERING is not indexed, but the reason for its inclusion is obvious. The list consists mainly of American Journals. It does not include the foreign equivalents of the MAGAZINE OF STANDARDS, official journal of the American Standards Association. The journals of foreign national standardizing bodies are discussed briefly in Section VI.

The brief annotations refer, generally, to the subject content of the articles on standards and specifications which appeared in the specific journal during the past six years.

ACTUAL SPECIFYING ENGINEER. Medalist Publications, Inc., 1801 Prairie Avenue, Chicago 16, Illinois. Monthly.
Specifications on air conditioning, heating, piping, plumbing, refrigeration, and ventilating.

AIR CONDITIONING, HEATING & REFRIGERATION NEWS.*

450 West Fort Street, Detroit 26, Michigan. Weekly.
News of standards development in the field; industry certification plans and programs.

AIR CONDITIONING, HEATING AND VENTILATING.* Industrial

Press, 93 Worth Street, New York, New York 10013. Monthly.
Plumbing codes; specifications for air conditioning, heating and ventilating equipment and components of systems.

AMERICAN DYESTUFF REPORTER. Howes Publishing Co., 44 E.

23rd Street, New York, New York 10010. Bi-weekly.
Discussions of standards relating to textile fabrics and dyes.

AMERICAN GAS ASSOCIATION MONTHLY. American Gas

Association, 605 Third Avenue, New York, New York 10016.
News of Association standards activities.

AMERICAN MACHINIST/METALWORKING MANUFACTURER.*

McGraw-Hill, Inc., 330 West 42nd Street, New York, New York

10036.
Discussions of standards on fasteners, screw threads, machine tool and measurements.

ARCHITECTURAL FORUM. Time, Inc., Rockefeller Center, New

York, New York 10020. Monthly.
Architectural specifications.

ARCHITECTURAL RECORD. McGraw-Hill, Inc., 330 West 42nd

Street, New York, New York 10036. Monthly.
Time-saver standards for the preparation of architectural specifications.

ARCHIVES OF ENVIRONMENTAL HEALTH. American Medical

Association, 535 North Dearborn Street, Chicago, Illinois

60610. Monthly.
Air quality standards; threshold limit values.

ASHRAE JOURNAL.* American Society of Heating, Refrigerating

and Air-Conditioning Engineers, 345 East 47th Street, New York,

New York. 10017 Monthly.
Regular Standards Page feature as well as technical articles and news items on standards deveiopment within the industry.

ASSEMBLY & FASTENER ENGINEERING. Hitchcock Publishing Co., Wheaton, Illinois. Monthly.
Fastener standards; time and motion studies.

AUTOMATION. Penton Publishing Co., Penton Building, Cleveland Cleveland 13, Ohio. Monthly.
Standardization in automatic processes and materials handling.

AUTOMOTIVE INDUSTRIES. Chilton Co., Chestnut & 56th Streets, Philadelphia 39, Pennsylvania. Semi-monthly.
Hydraulic and pneumatic standards; machine tool standardization.

BUILDING STANDARDS MONTHLY. International Conference of Building Officials, 50 South Los Robles St., Pasadena, California. Monthly.
Building codes.

CHEMICAL & ENGINEERING NEWS.* American Chemical Society, 1155 16th Street, N.W., Washington, D.C. 20036.
Reports developments on standardization affecting the chemical industry, e.g., nuclear and radiation safety standards, measurement standards, standards for chemical industry pumps; standards for machine searching of literature, and many other subjects.

CHEMICAL ENGINEERING. McGraw-Hill, Inc., 330 West 42nd Street, New York, New York 10036. Bi-weekly.
Chemical plant equipment standards; pressure piping; safety standards.

COMMUNICATIONS OF THE ASSOCIATION FOR COMPUTING MACHINERY,* 211 East 43rd Street, New York, New York 10017. Monthly.
Computer language and technology.

CONSTRUCTION SPECIFIER. Construction Specifications Institute, Dupont Circle Building, Washington 6, D.C. Monthly.
Legal and technical aspects of specifications writing.

CONTROL ENGINEERING. McGraw-Hill, Inc., 330 West 42nd Street, New York, New York 10036. Monthly.
Control standards.

DOMESTIC ENGINEERING. Medalist Publications, 1801 Prairie

Avenue, Chicago, Illinois 60616. Monthly.
Plumbing codes and standards.

ELECTRICAL CONSTRUCTION & MAINTENANCE.* McGraw-Hill, Inc., 330 West 42nd Street, New York, New York 10036.
Specifications for residential and industrial electrical equipment; selection of electrical system components with reference to National Electric Code and other standards.

ELECTRICAL WORLD.* McGraw-Hill, Inc., 330 West 42nd Street, New York, New York 10036. Weekly.
Specifications for industrial electrical equipment.

ELECTRONIC INDUSTRIES.* Chilton Co., Chestnut & 56th Streets, Philadelphia, Pennsylvania, 19139. Monthly.
Electronic apparatus and equipment. Special June issue (not published in 1964) has published lists of new electrical and electronic standards issued during the previous year.

ELECTRONIC NEWS. Fairchild Publications, 7 East 12th Street, New York, New York 10003. Weekly.
Developments in electrical and electronic equipment standards, especially in industries having military and space program contracts.

ELECTRONICS. McGraw-Hill, Inc., 330 West 42nd Street, New York, New York 10036. Bi-weekly.
Frequency standards; measurement and calibration; telemetry; variety of electrical and electronic apparatus.

ELECTRONICS WORLD. Ziff-Davis Publishing Co., One Park Avenue, New York, New York 10016. Monthly.
Frequency standards; measurement.

ELECTRO-TECHNOLOGY.* Conover-Mast Publications, 205 East 42nd Street, New York, New York 10017. Monthly.
Transformers; circuits for computers; measurement; shock tests.

ENGINEER.* Morgan Brothers, Ltd., 28 Essex Street, Strand, London W.C.2, England. Weekly.
Measurement; construction; electrical equipment; structural steel; transportation equipment.

ENGINEERING.* Engineering, Ltd., 36 Bedford Street, London W.C.2, England. Weekly.

Automobile engineering; construction; electrical equipment; measurement; machine tools; pressure vessels; drafting room practice.

ENGINEERING NEWS-RECORD.* McGraw-Hill, Inc., 330 West 42nd Street, New York, New York 10036. Weekly.
Building construction; structural steel; building codes; lumber.

FASTENERS. Industrial Fasteners Institute, 1517 Terminal Tower, Cleveland 13, Ohio. Quarterly.
Specifications for screws, bolts, locknuts and other industrial fasteners.

FEDERAL REGISTER. Government Printing Office, Washington, D.C. 20402.
Texts of standards and codes issued by regulatory agencies of the Federal Government.

FOOD DRUG COSMETIC LAW JOURNAL. Commerce Clearing House, 4025 West Peterson Avenue, Chicago 46, Illinois. Monthly.
Excellent source of information on food standards, codes, regulations and laws.

FOOD TECHNOLOGY. Institute of Food Technologists, P.O. Box 98, Davis, California 95616. Monthly.
Food standards.

FOUNDRY.* Penton Publishing Co., Penton Building, Cleveland 13, Ohio. Monthly.
Metal castings.

HEATING, PIPING & AIR CONDITIONING.* Keeney Publishing Co., 6 North Michigan Avenue, Chicago 2, Illinois. Monthly.
Air conditioning; piping; boilers.

HYDROCARBON PROCESSING AND PETROLEUM REFINER.* Gulf Publishing Co., Box 2608, Houston, Texas.
Specifying numerous items of refinery processing equipment.

ILLUMINATING ENGINEERING.* Illuminating Engineering Society, 345 East 47th Street, New York, New York 10017. Monthly.
Lighting standards.

INDUSTRIAL FINISHING. Practical Publications, 1142 North

Meridian Street, Indianapolis, Indiana 46204. Monthly.
Specifying paints and finishes for metals.

INSTRUMENTS & CONTROL SYSTEMS.* Instruments Publishing Co., 845 Ridge Avenue, Pittsburgh, Pennsylvania 15212. Monthly.
Standards laboratories; calibration; electrical standards; measurement.

IRON AGE.* Chilton Co., Chestnut & 56th Streets, Philadelphia, Pennsylvania 19139. Weekly.
Welding; fastening; screw threads; gearing; machine tools.

IRON & STEEL ENGINEER.* Association of Iron & Steel Engineers, 1010 Empire Building, Pittsburgh, Pennsylvania 15222. Monthly.
Cranes and derricks; electric motors; bearings; steel mill equipment.

ISA JOURNAL.* Instrument Society of America, Penn-Sheraton Hotel, 530 William Penn Place, Pittsburgh, Pennsylvania 15219. Monthly.
Standards laboratories; calibration and measurement standards.

JOURNAL OF MILK AND FOOD TECHNOLOGY. International Association of Milk, Food & Environmental Sanitarians, Box 437, Shelbyville, Indiana. Monthly.
Standards for dairy processing equipment; texts of 3-A Sanitary Standards Committee standards.

JOURNAL OF RESEARCH OF THE NATIONAL BUREAU OF STANDARDS.* Government Printing Office, Washington, D.C. 20402. Monthly in four parts.
Calibration, measurement, frequency and radiation standards.

JOURNAL OF THE AIR POLLUTION CONTROL ASSOCIATION. Air Pollution Control Association, 4400 Fifth Avenue, Pittsburgh 13, Pennsylvania. Monthly.
Air quality standards; automobile exhaust.

JOURNAL OF THE AMERICAN CONCRETE INSTITUTE.* American Concrete Institute, P.O. Box 4754, Bedford Station, Detroit 19, Michigan. Monthly.
Building code requirements for concrete; standards on concrete and concrete construction.

JOURNAL OF THE AMERICAN SOCIETY OF SAFETY ENGINEERS. American Society of Safety Engineers, 5 North Wabash Avenue, Chicago, Illinois. 60602. Monthly.

Safety standards. Article in October 1964 issue announced appointment of 12 committees to review safety standards.

JOURNAL OF THE AMERICAN WATER WORKS ASSOCIATION.* American Water Works Association, 2 Park Avenue, New York, New York 10016. Monthly.

Water quality; standards for water pipe and other water supply systems equipment.

JOURNAL OF THE AUDIO ENGINEERING SOCIETY. Audio Engineering Society, P.O. Box 383, Madison Square Station, New York, New York 10010. Quarterly.

Standards of measurement for high fidelity system components; standards for stereo tape.

JOURNAL OF THE SMPTE.* Society of Motion Picture and Television Engineers, 9 East 41st Street, New York, New York 10017. Monthly.

Motion picture recording, films, machines, photography; television transmission.

LUBRICATION ENGINEERING. American Society of Lubrication Engineers, 838 Busse Highway, Park Ridge, Illinois 60068. Monthly.

Standards for lubricants and lubrication.

MACHINE DESIGN.* Penton Publishing Co., Penton Building, Cleveland, Ohio 44113. Bi-weekly.

Drafting room practice; fasteners; measurement; specification writing.

MACHINERY.* Industrial Press, 93 Worth Street, New York, New York 10013. Monthly.

Machine tools; specifications for metals.

MAGAZINE OF STANDARDS.* American Standards Association, 10 East 40th Street, New York, New York 10016. Monthly.

Its broad range of coverage of standards activities include articles on the development of specific American Standards; reports of company standards programs; standardization work of trade associations and technical societies; international standardization and standards in foreign countries. Regular features are "Cross-Indexing Industry and Military Specifications and Standards," "Standards from Other Countries," "American Standards Projects," "Newly Published American Standards," "American Standards Under Way," "New International "Recommendations."

MATERIALS IN DESIGN ENGINEERING.* Reinhold Publishing Corp., 420 Park Avenue, New York, New York 10022. Monthly.

Specifications for metals and alloys.

MATERIALS RESEARCH AND STANDARDS* (Formerly ASTM Bulletin). American Society for Testing and Materials, 1916 Race Street, Philadelphia, Pennsylvania 19103. Monthly.

A broad range of technical, news and general items dealing with standards and specifications, such as standards in building construction; specifications for metals; water quality; developments relative to ASTM standards; legal aspects of standardization, and many others.

MILL & FACTORY.* Conover-Mast Publications, 205 East 42nd Street, New York, New York 10017. Monthly.

Engineered performance standards.

MODERN MATERIALS HANDLING. 221 Columbus Avenue, Boston, Massachusetts 02116. Monthly.

Containers and pallets.

MODERN PACKAGING. 770 Lexington Avenue, New York, New York 10021. Monthly.

Containers for shipping; packaging.

MODERN PLASTICS.* Breskin Publications, 770 Lexington Avenue, New York, New York 10021. Monthly.

International plastics standardization activities; annual "Year in Review" feature includes a discussion of new standards.

MECHANICAL ENGINEERING.* American Society of Mechanical Engineers, 345 East 47th Street, New York, New York 10017. Monthly.

ASME boiler and pressure code interpretations and changes; code for pressure piping; containers for shipping; measurements.

METAL FINISHING.* Metals and Plastics Publications, 99 Kinderkamack Road, Westwood, New Jersey 07675. Monthly.
Finishing to government specifications.

METAL PROGRESS.* American Society for Metals, Metals Park, Ohio 44072. Monthly.
Specifications for steel castings and forgings; metal plating; heat treatment; alloys.

METALLURGIA. Kennedy Press, Ltd., 31 King Street, West Manchester 3, England. Monthly.
Metals and alloys.

NTDRA DEALER NEWS. National Tire Dealers and Retreaders Association, 1343 L Street, N.W., Washington 5, D.C. Weekly.
Developments in standards for automobile tires and retreads.

PLANT ENGINEERING.* Technical Publishing Co., 308 East James Street, Barrington, Illinois 60010. Monthly.
Construction specifications.

PLASTICS WORLD. Cleworth Publishing Co., 1 River Road, Cos Cob, Connecticut 06807. Monthly.
Plastic materials standards and specifications.

POWER. McGraw-Hill, Inc., 330 West 42nd Street, New York, New York 10036. Monthly.
Pipes and piping; electric equipment.

POWER APPARATUS & SYSTEMS.* Institute of Electrical and Electronics Engineers, 72 West 45th Street, New York, New York 10036. Bi-monthly.
Electrical distribution systems.

PROCEEDINGS OF THE AMERICAN SOCIETY OF CIVIL ENGINEERS. American Society of Civil Engineers, 345 East 47th Street, New York, New York 10017. Monthly.
Specifications for structural components.

PROCEEDINGS OF THE INSTITUTE OF ELECTRICAL AND ELECTRONICS ENGINEERS,* Institute of Electrical and Electronics Engineers, 72 West 45th Street, New York, New York 10036.
Measurement, tolerance, and calibration standards for a broad variety of electrical and electronic apparatus.

PRODUCT ENGINEERING.* McGraw-Hill, Inc., 330 West 42nd Street, New York, New York 10036. Monthly.
Machine tools and a wide variety of industrial apparatus and equipment.

PROGRESSIVE ARCHITECTURE.* Reinhold Publishing Corp., 430 Park Avenue, New York, New York 10022. Monthly.
Construction specifications.

PUBLIC WORKS.* 200 South Broad Street, Ridgewood, New Jersey 07450. Monthly.
Roads and roadmaking materials and machinery.

PURCHASING. Conover-Mast Publications, 205 East 42nd Street, New York, New York 10017. Bi-weekly.
Importance of standardization to purchasing process.

QUICK FROZEN FOODS.* E. W. Williams Publications, 1776 Broadway, New York, New York 10019. Monthly.
Standards for foods and food products; frozen food handling codes.

ROADS AND STREETS.* Reuben H. Donnelley Corp., 466 Lexington Avenue, New York, New York 10017. Monthly.
Road construction and road materials specifications.

SAE JOURNAL.* Society of Automotive Engineers, 485 Lexington Avenue, New York, New York 10017. Monthly.
Automobile components; machine tools; tolerances; measurements; aerospace standards.

SAFETY MAINTENANCE.* Alfred M. Best Co., 75 Fulton Street, New York, New York 10038. Monthly.
Safety standards.

SAFETY STANDARDS. Government Printing Office, Washington, D.C. 20402. Bi-monthly.
Publications of the U.S. Bureau of Labor Standards dealing with industrial safety standards.

SPE JOURNAL. Society of Plastics Engineers, 65 Prospect Street, Stamford, Connecticut. Monthly.
Plastics and plastic materials specifications.

STANDARDS ENGINEERING. Standards Engineer Society, 170 Livingston Avenue, New Providence, New Jersey. Monthly.
General, news, and technical articles dealing with all

aspects of standards, both here and abroad; particular emphasis on standardization activities at the company level.

STEEL.* Penton Publishing Co., Penton Building, Cleveland, Ohio 44113. Weekly.
Fasteners; castings; structural steel; machine tools.

TAPPI.* Technical Association of the Pulp and Paper Industry, 360 Lexington Avenue, New York, New York 10017. Monthly.
Paper and pulp products; processing machinery and equipment.

TECHNICAL NEWS BULLETIN. Government Printing Office, Washington, D.C. 20402. Monthly.
Published by the U.S. Bureau of Standards. Regular feature on standard materials and calibration and measurement standards.

TOOL AND MANUFACTURING ENGINEER.* American Society of Tool and Manufacturing Engineers, 10700 Puritan Avenue, Detroit, Michigan 48238. Monthly.
Machine tools; economics derived from standardization.

TRANSACTIONS OF THE AMERICAN SOCIETY OF MECHANICAL ENGINEERS, 345 East 47th Street, New York, New York 10017. Quarterly in 5 parts.
Standards of design and measurement in a variety of engineering fields.

WELDING ENGINEER. Welding Engineer, P.O. Box 28, Morton Grove, Illinois 60053. Monthly.
Welding.

WELDING JOURNAL. American Welding Society, 345 East 47th Street, New York, New York 10017. Monthly.
Welding.

AUTHOR –TITLE INDEX

AUTHOR – TITLE INDEX

A

AUTHOR –TITLE INDEX

B

C

D

E

F

G

H

I

N

O

P

Q

R

S

T

Y

Z

SUBJECT INDEX

SUBJECT INDEX

C

D

E

F

G

H

I

T

U

V

W

Y

Z

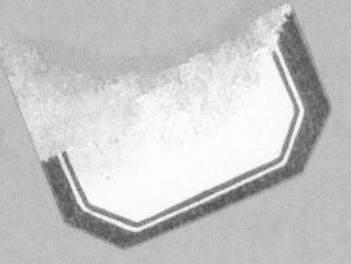